POEMS OF EDGAR ALLAN POE

POEMS OF
EDGAR ALLAN POE

Selected by Dwight Macdonald

Drawings by Ellen Raskin

THOMAS Y. CROWELL COMPANY • NEW YORK

CONTENTS

INTRODUCTION

When in 1849 Edgar Allan Poe died in a Baltimore hospital, at forty, of what was then called *delirium tremens* ("the DT's"), he left behind a body of work as contradictory as his life had been. The arguments are still going on. His alcoholism, to begin with. The legend that he wrote under the influence of liquor is a legend. Poe was an alcoholic who couldn't drink; a small amount would send him into frenzied incoherence. Most of the time he drank nothing stronger than tea, but every so often, for psychological reasons we still know little about, he went off on a "spree," as his family called it, though nothing could have been less spreelike than those joyless, compulsive drinking bouts that ruined his career and finally killed him. A few years ago, another poet died in another American hospital after another long drunk. Poe's doctors called it "acute congestion of the brain," but the diagnosis of those who attended Dylan Thomas was more imaginative, and accurate: "a massive insult to the brain."

A journalist as industrious as he was brilliant, a critic who won a national reputation with his first reviews, an editor who made quick successes of three magazines, a poet and essayist and short-story writer whose work was widely read (and widely pirated), Edgar Allan Poe was a highly successful professional writer in every way except one: his work seldom earned him enough to escape the most wretched poverty. *The Raven* made him famous overnight, like Byron with *Childe Harold*, and remained our most popular poem well into this century. Some biographers say he received $5 for it; others think it may have been $10. In 1929, the manuscript was sold in London for $100,000.

Such ironies are familiar in literary history, but in Poe's case they really go too far. At another London auction, in 1963, a youthful letter he had written to Washington Irving fetched the top price of the sale. It was a begging letter, from an obscure beginner to the then Dean of American Letters. Excusing himself for intruding—"an utter stranger"—Poe, noting that his tale, *William Wilson*, was "based upon a brief article of your

1

own," asks the great man for a blurb: "even a word or two from yourself [and] my fortune would be made." "I have read your little tale with much pleasure," Irving replied. "It is managed in a highly picturesque style, and the singular and mysterious interest is well-sustained." This cautious encomium did not make Poe's fortune, however. His shade, and if ever an author has a right to a shade it is Poe, must have smiled grimly when a century later his begging note sold for $5,600, enough to have kept him in comfort for years.

Poe's literary character was also paradoxical. He was the most unromantic of romantics, pushing his subject matter to the wildest "Gothic" extremes while his method of composition was classically controlled. A neurotic whose obsessions verged on madness, he had a mind of exceptional clarity which he used not to escape from his obsessions or to subdue them but to transcend them, boldly making them the motive power of an *oeuvre* that is still argued about, and read, as intensely today as if he had died in 1949 and not in 1849. There has always been extreme disagreement about its literary value, more than in the case of any other major American writer—it is interesting that his severest critics somehow take it for granted that Poe *is* major—but I think a few statements may be safely made:

—that Poe was our only major poet before Whitman.

—that he was our first serious critic, writing with an intellectual rigor and a close analysis of the text that was not to reappear until the thirties with the "New Criticism" of Ransom, Brooks, and Warren (if only they had also had his wit!). In Edmund Wilson's opinion, it was "the most remarkable body of criticism ever produced in the United States, our only first-rate classical prose of the period."

—that he wrote a number of tales which, despite a lush rhetoric that now seems old-fashioned, continue to be read because the drive of his obsessed mind carried them far beyond the merely picturesque effects of his early models, the German romantic school of E. T. A. Hoffmann. "Their terror is not of Germany, but of the soul," as he himself observes.

—that he was a pioneer in those borderlands which have come

to interest us as science has developed beyond the materialistic limits of his time—limits he mocked or ignored—and that he often ventured into the mistiest borderland of all, between conscious and unconscious, natural and supernatural, life and death.

—that he worked out in his criticism and exemplified in his creation theories which were both new and influential. "He stands as one of the few great innovators in American literature," F. O. Matthiessen concludes his fine chapter on Poe in the Canby-Spiller-Thorpe *History of American Literature*. "Like Henry James and T. S. Eliot, he took his place, almost from the start, in international culture as an original creative force."

The life of Edgar Allan Poe has often been told: he has been the subject of more, and worse, biographies than any other American writer. It is a paradigm of the self-destroying genius, *le poète maudit*, and it arouses the worst instincts for melodrama —as if anything could be more sensational than the unadorned facts. The best short life is still George Woodberry's (1885). By far the best long one is Arthur Hobson Quinn's *Edgar Allan Poe, a Critical Biography* (1941). The interest of Poe's life for the present purpose is its intimate connection with his work, and especially with his poetry.

Edgar Poe was born in 1809 in Boston, where his young actor-parents were playing in a traveling repertory company. His mother, Elizabeth Arnold, was of British birth; his father, David Poe, Jr., who deserted his wife the following year and of whom no trace has been found afterwards, was the ne'er-do-well son of a respected Baltimore citizen who had been a quartermaster-general in Washington's army and a comrade-in-arms of Lafayette. Elizabeth Poe died two years later in Richmond, Virginia, and her three-year-old boy was adopted by John Allan, a prosperous merchant whose wife had befriended Mrs. Poe. The boy came to love his stepmother and to detest his stepfather. (He rarely used his middle name, signing himself "Edgar A. Poe.") So the pattern was set almost before he could talk—Poe's biography is as strictly unified as his poems and tales: the antagonism to men (he seems never to have had a close male friend) and the

3

emotional dependence on women, his father deserting him, his mother cherishing him, and his step-parents falling into the same relationships.

In 1815 the Allans moved to England, where Edgar was sent to private schools, one of which is described at length in *William Wilson*, a story of double identity that was one of Stevenson's sources for *Dr. Jekyll and Mr. Hyde*, as *The Gold Bug* was for *Treasure Island*. The family returned to Richmond in 1820. Three years later, at fourteen, Poe experienced his first "ideal love"— for Mrs. Jane Stannard, the young mother of a schoolmate. She was kind to him, the first of a long line of female confidantes. When she died the next year, he may or may not have haunted her grave as he later claimed—Poe was given to romance about his past—but there is no question her death affected him deeply, and permanently. As Woodberry writes, "Her loss was the ground on which his imagination long worked, and determined the early bent of his mind toward a sombre supernaturalism." In 1826 Poe entered the University of Virginia. He did well in studies but drank and ran up gambling debts—Woodberry puts them at $2,500, a huge sum then and impressive even now— which Mr. Allan refused to pay, withdrawing his stepson from the University. It was a disastrous year. Before leaving for college, Poe had become engaged to a neighbor's daughter, Sarah Elmira Royster, but her parents, disapproving, intercepted his letters and she, thinking he had lost interest, married someone else. The social snub may have been as painful to Poe as losing the girl—he was always touchy about such matters; in any case, it was another psychic wound, and another recurrent theme in his poetry.

The years 1827 to 1830 are obscure, some months being still unaccounted for, though not enough to make believable his story about traveling to Moscow and later taking part in the Greek insurrection against the Turks. What is known is that he refused a clerkship in Mr. Allan's business, went to Boston where he managed to get published, or rather printed, *Tamerlane and Other Poems* (1827), enlisted as a private in the army under a false name, rose to sergeant-major in two years, became recon-

4

ciled enough with his stepfather for Mr. Allan to use his influence to get him honorably discharged and—after a year of which the only significant event that is known is the publication of *Al Aaraaf, Tamerlane and Minor Poems* (Baltimore, 1829)—to have him enrolled as a cadet at West Point in the spring of 1830. But Mrs. Allan had died in 1829 and her husband remarried the following year, ending whatever frail hopes of inheritance Poe may still have had and causing Mr. Allan's remittances to become even more niggardly than usual. Although his academic standing was high, Poe was unable to pay for essentials like laundry. "The army does not suit a poor man," he observed. After deliberately cutting classes and parades, he was court-martialed and expelled early in 1831. A few months later, he published his third slender volume, *Poems by Edgar A. Poe* (New York, 1831), "dedicated to the cadets of West Point" whose subscriptions had paid the printer's bill. It was a unique event in our military history, which resumed its normal course when the cadets received the book. They didn't like it.

In the summer of 1831, Poe changed his life in two ways that were to be permanent until his death eighteen years later.

He was forced by economic necessity to turn from poetry to prose, becoming a successful editor and a journalist who turned out anything he thought might "go": stories, humorous extravaganzas like *The Man that Was Used Up* and *Never Bet the Devil Your Head*, reviews, sketches of the New York literati (with "character-readings" from their signatures), a poem like *The Raven*—so bad, and so popular, that I cannot believe it was not written with an eye to the market—and newspaper stunts like his "Balloon Hoax" in the *N.Y. Sun* of April 13, 1844, an imaginary account of the first transatlantic air flight ("ASTOUNDING NEWS BY EXPRESS, VIA NORFOLK! THE ATLANTIC CROSSED IN THREE DAYS, SIGNAL TRIUMPH OF MR. MONCK MASON'S FLYING MACHINE! ARRIVAL AT SULLIVAN'S ISLAND, NEAR CHARLESTON, S.C.!") that was so minutely circumstantial as to cause mob scenes around the paper's offices. (Cooler heads may have remembered that Sullivan's Island was the scene of *The Gold Bug*, another plausible fiction Poe had published the year before.) It is hard to say which is the most striking aspect of Poe's career as a literary journalist, its success in terms of readers, its failure in terms of money (for *The Gold Bug*, his most popular tale—he estimated "more than 300,000 copies have been circulated"—*Graham's Magazine* paid him $52), or the persistence and ingenuity with which he transformed hack writing into his own personal expression. Into, in fact, literature. His one novel, for example, *The Narrative of A. Gordon Pym*, a masterpiece that has had to wait even longer than *Moby Dick* for recognition, was undertaken from the most commercial calculations. Poe had sent Harper's a collection of his tales, which they had refused, writing him that "our long experience has taught us [such collections] are the most unsaleable of all literary performances," as is still the case, and suggesting that, as is also still true: "Readers in this country have a decided and strong preference for works (especially fiction) in which a single and connected story occupies the whole volume." And so Poe wrote *Pym*, which Harper's published, equipped with a "selling" title-page (with no objection from the author) that promised among other things, "Details of a Mutiny and Atrocious Butchery. . . . Shipwreck and subsequent Horrible Sufferings from Famine. . . . Massacre . . . incredible Adventures and Discoveries." But masterpieces are notoriously hard to sell, and *Pym* did little better than *Moby Dick* ten years later.

The other change in Poe's life was more important. In the summer of 1831, he went to live with his aunt, Mrs. Clemm, and her nine-year-old daughter, Virginia. For the rest of his life, Mrs. Clemm devoted her practical talents, which were considerable, to making an orderly, cheerful home for her beloved "Eddie," skillfully managing the small and irregular earnings got by so much work and keeping things together in crises by making the rounds of friends and publishers to ask for small advances, loans, or even a ham or turkey to put into her market basket; not an agreeable occupation for a Baltimore gentlewoman, with whatever dignity Mrs. Clemm carried it off. Poe had found a mother again. Five years later he found a wife, marrying Virginia shortly before her fourteenth birthday. But if Mrs. Clemm was his mother, as she was in every way except literally, her daughter becomes Poe's sister—she was in fact, of course, his first cousin —and indeed his attitude seems to have been less that of a husband than of an affectionate older (by thirteen years) brother to an admiring young sister. That Poe's relations with women were peculiar is as obvious as that their influence on his life and work was profound. Much has been written on the subject, including a psychoanalytic biography by Dr. Marie Bonaparte that explains, or seems to, many things. There has been no lack of speculation, scholarly and otherwise, about child brides (though Virginia was twenty-five when she died), mother fixation, and other intriguing aspects of Poe's unconscious. Many of these hypotheses are interesting, some are even reasonable, but— aside from the fact that Poe died seven years before Freud was born and so was never observed by anyone with even a layman's knowledge of Freudian theory—the term "unconscious" suggests a realm that, by definition, is more appropriate to speculations than to conclusions. At the head of *The Murders in the Rue Morgue*, Poe put a tag from Sir Thomas Browne's *Urn-Burial:* "What song the Syrens sang, or what name Achilles assumed when he hid himself among the women, although puzzling questions are not beyond *all* conjecture." He emphasized *"all"* to suit his tale of ratiocination, but when it comes to the inwardness of his relations with Mrs. Clemm and Virginia, I would italicize *"conjecture"* and *"puzzling."* The only real data we have, superficial from a Freudian standpoint and scanty from any, are his own letters and the written accounts of his contemporaries, and they all point to the same conclusion: that he was as selflessly devoted to Virginia and Mrs. Clemm as they were to him. My own speculations are that his efforts to support them, which for a man of his temperament may be called heroic, gave him a motive for writing, perhaps even for living; that this strange *ménage à trois* was the one great success of his private life, as against his literary career; and that, for the fifteen years it lasted, it provided him, for the first and only time, with some degree of psychological equilibrium. I think Baudelaire did not exaggerate in the dedication to Mrs. Clemm of a volume of his Poe translations when he saluted her as "a mother whose greatness and goodness honors the world of letters as much as the marvelous creations of her son . . . the woman who was always so gentle and kind to him—as you bound his wounds with your love, so he will preserve your name with his glory."

As for the shadowy Virginia, of whom we know little more than that she was beautiful, passive, silent, and loving—and that during the winter she was dying of consumption in the little white cottage at Fordham she was warmed by a large tortoise-shell cat crouching on her chest—as for Virginia, whether the marriage was "consummated" or not, her death upset the precarious balance of Poe's life. He died after three chaotic years in which he courted various matrons, became engaged to two, and broke both engagements by going on drunken "sprees." The last and fatal one burst like a thunderclap from a clear sky after he had made a sentimental pilgrimage to Richmond, where he was lionized, giving his lecture on *The Poetic Principle* with success there and in Norfolk, meeting his old love, Sarah Royster, now a widow, proposing again to her, successfully, and, on September 27, 1849, taking the boat to New York to arrange with Mrs. Clemm the details of the marriage. Six days later, an interval of which little is known, an acquaintance found him wandering in the streets of Baltimore "rather the worse for wear" and took him to the Washington College Hospital, where he died on October 7.

"It is in the historic rather than in the critical estimate that his eminence appears," W. C. Brownell wrote of Poe in his influential *American Prose Masters* (1909), adding that Poe's writings "lack the elements not only of great, but of real, literature" and that they are "essentially valueless." Allowing for polemical exaggeration—after all, he devotes a whole chapter to this "essentially valueless" author—this is a fair summary of the American Literary Establishment's opinion of Poe.

Emerson called him "the jingle man" and left him out of his anthology, *The American Parnassus* (1847), as did William Cullen

Bryant from his *Selections from the American Poets* (1840). (Mr. Bryant may have had nonliterary reasons. He refused to contribute to a memorial to mark Poe's grave in Baltimore: "I think there should be some decided element of goodness in the character of those to whom a public monument directs the attention of the world.") James Russell Lowell, the only important man of letters of Poe's time who admired his work and was in friendly correspondence with him, could find nothing better to say about him in *A Fable for Critics* than:

> Here comes Poe with his Raven, like Barnaby Rudge—
> Three-fifths of him genius and two-fifths sheer fudge;
> Who talks like a book of iambs and pentameters
> In a way to make all men of common sense d---n metres;
> Who has written some things far the best of his kind,
> But somehow the heart seems squeezed out by the mind.*

Walt Whitman was the only prominent writer who attended the dedication, in 1875, of that Poe memorial Bryant had deplored ten years earlier—raising the funds was evidently a slow business. It was all the more to Whitman's credit that he attended

---

* On which Poe, in a review of the *Fable:* "We may observe here that profound ignorance on any particular topic is always sure to manifest itself by some allusion to 'common sense' as an all-suffcient instructor. So far from Mr. P.'s talking 'like a book' on the topic at issue, his chief purpose has been to demonstrate that there exist *no* book on the subject worth talking *about;* and 'common sense,' after all, has been the basis on which *he* relied, in contradistinction from the uncommon nonsense of Mr. L. and the small pedants."

I think Poe was right when he claimed that "common sense" was on *his* side here, the real kind, which criticizes abstractions by bringing concrete reality to bear on them. His reference—and Lowell's—is to "The Rationale of Verse," too long and technical to be included in these selections, which shows, with a richness of examples, that the commonly accepted prosody of his day—which he calls "scholastic scansion" because it was derived from Latin verse on the false assumption that Latin was a universal model for all languages—made no sense when it was applied to English verse. The grammarians of the period were, on the same false premise, trying to force English usage into the straitjacket of Latin.

since he felt little sympathy for a poet who was in every way his opposite: "Among the electric lights of literature," was his summary, "brilliant and dazzling, with no heat." Our greatest modern poet and critic, the late T. S. Eliot, has been most severe of all: "If we examine his work in detail, we seem to find in it nothing but slipshod writing, puerile thinking unsupported by wide reading or profound scholarship, haphazard experiments in various types of writing, chiefly under pressure of financial need, without perfection in any detail. . . . That Poe has a powerful intellect is undeniable, but it seems to me the intellect of a highly gifted young person before puberty." On these sweeping judgments by the usually circumspect Mr. Eliot—I have not been fortunate enough to meet any pre-pubertal "highly gifted young person"—that is, a boy aged thirteen or less, or a girl aged eleven or less—whose intellect reminded me of Poe's.

Except for Yeats, who called Poe "always and for all lands a great lyric poet," the English Establishment has also been cool. D. H. Lawrence's chapter on Poe in his *Studies in Classic American Literature* is a mixture of pity and contempt. His psychological insights are often acute, but his chief literary comment is:

> Poe has been praised for his style. But it seems to me a meretricious affair. "Her marble hand" and "the elasticity of her footfall" in *Ligeia* seem more like chair-springs and mantelpieces than a human creature. . . . All Poe's style, moreover, has this mechanical quality, as his poetry has a mechanical rhythm. He never sees anything in terms of life, almost always in terms of matter, jewels, marble, etc. —or in terms of force, scientific. And his cadences are all managed mechanically. This is what is called "having a style."

One might retort that Lawrence's own work might have gained had he worried more about "having a style," but his description of Poe's style seems to me valid, as far as it goes. As does, as far as it goes, Aldous Huxley's paragraph, in his essay, *The Vulgarity of Poe:*

> The substance of Poe is refined; it is his form that is vulgar. He is, as it were, one of Nature's Gentlemen, unhappily cursed with

incorrigible bad taste. To the most sensitive and high-souled man in the world we should find it hard to forgive, shall we say, the wearing of a diamond ring on every finger. Poe does the equivalent of this in his poetry; we notice the solecism and shudder. Foreign observers do not notice it; they detect only the native gentleman-liness in the poetical intention, not the vulgarity in the details of execution. To them we seem perversely and quite incomprehensibly unjust.

To me the Anglo-American Establishment seems quite comprehensibly unjust to Poe; which brings us to those "foreign observers."

"I have discovered an American writer who arouses in me an unbelievable sympathy," Baudelaire wrote his mother in 1852, "and I have written two articles on his life and work." The articles appeared in the *Revue de Paris* and marked the beginning of the influence of Poe on French Symbolism, which Mr. Eliot has called "the most important movement in the world of poetry since Wordsworth and Coleridge." (Not the least evidence of its importance was its influence on Mr. Eliot's own poetry, especially *The Wasteland*.) For three generations of symbolist poets, from Baudelaire to Valéry, Poe was the founding father: the lawgiver who had first laid down the basic theories of their school and the master whose works illustrate those theories. "Here is the literature of the twentieth century," the De Goncourts wrote in their *Journal* shortly after Poe's death. For Baudelaire, Poe was more than an "influence." He prayed nightly to his mother and to Edgar Poe. He translated *Eureka, A. Gordon Pym, The Raven*, and several volumes of the tales. "I am being accused, I, of imitating Edgar Poe," he wrote a friend. "Do you know why I translated Poe so patiently? Because he was like me. The first time I opened one of his books, I was shocked and delighted to see not only subjects which I had dreamed of but also *sentences* which I had thought and which he had written twenty years before."

In the next generation, Mallarmé translated the poems, describing Poe in his preface as "a genius who is the equal of our dearest and most respected masters." In a letter to a friend enclosing his sonnet, *L'Azure*, his first success in what was to become his distinctive style, Mallarmé wrote: "The more I continue in this direction, the more faithful I shall be to those severe ideas which I owe to my great master, Edgar Poe." As the other symbolists had, Verlaine adopted as his credo the disjunction of poetry from both truth and morality first proposed by Poe in *The Poetic Principle*, and, as they all did, he got his Poe direct. "We are learning English like mad, Rimbaud and I," he wrote in 1873 from London, "in Edgar Poe, in collections of popular songs." The last great symbolist poet, Paul Valéry, idolized Poe almost as much as had the first. In a youthful letter introducing himself to Mallarmé, he recites the litany: "I prize the theories of Poe, so profound and so insidiously learned; I believe in the omnipotence of rhythm, and especially in the suggestive phrase." His faith never wavered. "Poe is the only impeccable master," he wrote to André Gide many years later. "He was never mistaken."

The most common, and obvious, explanation of this difference of opinion between the French—and, to a lesser extent, the Russians and the Germans—and ourselves is that they don't know English as well as we do. Even the subtle Mr. Eliot, in *From Poe to Valéry* (in the Fall, 1949, *Hudson Review*) a scrupulously fair-minded attempt to explain why poets he admires admire a poet he doesn't admire, concludes simply that "None of these poets [Baudelaire, Mallarmé, Valéry] knew the English language very well." He gives some persuasive evidence, and I must admit that when M. Valéry calls Poe "the only impeccable master," adding "He was never mistaken," I am bewildered, for I can think of few masters who were more peccable, who strike more false notes, who are more often stylistically "mistaken." But I also think that Poe *was* a master, that his peccable style often rises to beauty and originality—that, in short, language differences are not enough to explain the problem.

It may be approached through another observation of Mr. Eliot, who seems to have been as obsessed by Poe as Baudelaire, though in the opposite direction. In his foreword to Joseph Chiari's

Symbolisme from Poe to Mallarmé, he broadens his attack, still stressing language: "How good a poet was Poe? There is no poet whose status is more disputed. And as a philosopher . . . ? We suspect, indeed, that if French poets had known the English language better, they might have based their esthetic not on that of Poe but on that of Coleridge." It is true that Coleridge was a more subtle and profound literary theoretician than Poe, who borrowed some of his ideas with slight or even sneering acknowledgment, a painful contrast to Baudelaire's generous insistence on his debt to Poe. But Poe had one quality that Coleridge notoriously lacked: the ability, and the daring, to simplify his ideas, to concentrate them into decisive formulations that rang like trumpet calls. It may have been the difference between Coleridge's neuroses and Poe's, or between a young literature and an old one, or the greater effort required to arouse to action the more massive intellect of Coleridge. I wonder, for instance, whether Poe was thinking of Coleridge when he wrote in *Marginalia:* "There are some facts in the physical world which have a really wonderful analogy with others in the world of thought. . . . It is not more true, in the former, that a large body is with more difficulty set in motion than a smaller one, and that its subsequent impetus is commensurate with this difficulty, than it is, in the latter, that intellects of the vaster capacity, while more forcible, more constant, and more extensive in their movements than those of inferior grade, are yet the less readily moved, and are more embarrassed and full of hesitation in the first few steps of their progress."

Whatever the reason, the fact is that Poe was a propagandist of genius, a polemicist who could broaden, and deepen, the pettiest quarrels so as to bring into play his revolutionary theories. His critical ideas, always clearly formulated and forcibly expressed, sounded the battle-cry for generations of French symbolists who found, to their amazement, that they were rebelling against the same *idées reçues*—what Professor Galbraith calls "the conventional wisdom"—that this isolated writer across the Atlantic had long before them identified as The Enemy and had been fighting alone, and without the help of a movement.

13

"For Poe, the United States was a vast cage, a great counting house," Baudelaire writes. "Dazzling a young and unformed country by his mind, shocking men who considered themselves his equals by his manners, he was fated to become a most unhappy writer. Rancors were aroused, solitude settled around him. In Paris, in Germany, he would have found friends who could easily have understood and comforted him, in America, he had to fight for his bread. Thus his drunkenness and his nomadic habits are easily explained. He went through life like a wanderer in the Sahara, changing his residence like an Arab."

And there is something else. Poe's appeal, his charm, his literary charisma is—ultimately—personal. Just what one wouldn't expect in a propagandist—but the uniting of opposites was his speciality. He committed himself to everything he wrote, transposing his neuroses into the impersonal key of art or journalism: he invented the detective story as a saleable commodity but it also served his private purposes, indulging his fascination with horror and death while also confining it safely under the control of reason ("ratiocination"); few poets have taken their themes more directly from their own lives, and few have treated them in a more deliberately artificial style worked out according to a theory. Poe's works are the autobiography of an obsessed neurotic, but because any truly individual expression, however strange and narrow, will strike home to other individuals, Poe has always had his addicts, from Baudelaire, with his "because he is like me," to Allen Tate, who ends his essay, *Our Cousin, Mr. Poe:* "He is so close to me that I am sometimes tempted to find out whether he may not actually be my cousin." I, too, have felt this kinship ever since, as a schoolboy at Phillips Exeter Academy, I read through the handsome, wide-margined "Amontillado" edition of Poe on weekend afternoons in the Davis Library.

Poetry was Poe's natural voice. But after the 1831 *Poems* had attracted as little attention as its two predecessors—that is, none —and after Mrs. Allan's death and Mr. Allan's remarriage had removed even that shaky financial prop, the twenty-three-year-old Poe had to turn to journalism. His prose often resembled poetry, and he continued to write poems (some of the most famous and some of the best—not identical categories—came after 1831) and to revise his earlier verse so meticulously that in the most extreme instance, *A Dream within a Dream*, not a single line of the 1827 original survives in the 1849 revision. (The version given here is the latter, which is much the better poem.) But prose was his profession not his vocation, his necessity rather than his choice, no matter how well he wrote it. There is real pathos as well as self-pitying rhetoric in his preface to his fourth, and last, collection of verse, *The Raven and Other Poems* (1845), which begins "These trifles . . ." and concludes: "I think nothing in this volume of much value to the public or very creditable to myself. Events not to be controlled have prevented me from making, at any time, serious efforts in what, under happier circumstances, would have been the field of my choice. With me, poetry has been not a purpose but a passion; and the passions must be held in reverence; they must not—they cannot at will be excited, with an eye to the paltry compensations, or the more paltry commendations of mankind."

Henry James, who thought that "an enthusiasm for Poe is the mark of a decidedly primitive stage of reflection," dismissed his poems as "very valueless verses," a phrase which Poe, at his most jingly, would have scorned. James later substituted "superficial" for "valueless," which got rid of the alliteration only to fall into absurdity, for if ever a poet wrote from the depths of his heart, or his unconscious, it was Poe. When he observed, in *The Philosophy of Composition*, "The death of a beautiful woman is unquestionably the most poetical topic in the world," he was thinking less of esthetics than of the deaths of his mother and Mrs. Stannard and of the illness of Virginia, who died the following year. And he was thinking of himself when he chose as a motto for *Ligeia* a quotation from the mystic, Joseph Glanvill: "And the will therein lieth, which dieth not. Who knoweth the mysteries of the will, with its vigor? For God is but a great Will pervading all things by nature of its intentness. Man doth not yield himself to the angels, nor unto death utterly, save only

15

through the weakness of his feeble will." D. H. Lawrence was right when he said "this was the clue to him." Poe was able to triumph over his inner disorder by creating in his writings an imaginary universe on which he was able to impose a high degree of order by the exercise of his will.

"Where then is the force in Poe that will explain the extremes of his active reputation?" R. P. Blackmur asks. "Let us say to begin with that Poe gives us a chance at a make-believe world and that he seems also to be about the business of remaking the world within his own scope if not quite in his own image, thus satisfying what children and French symbolist poets are supposed to be up to." Creating a world "in his own image" suggests God, and Mr. Blackmur's "if not quite" is too cautious. In that extraordinary cosmological treatise, *Eureka,* Poe quotes from an obscure French philosopher: "We know absolutely nothing of the nature or essence of God; to comprehend what He is, we should have to be God ourselves." Poe accepts the challenge: *"We should have to be God ourselves!* With a phrase so startling as this ringing in my ears, I nevertheless venture to demand if this our present ignorance of the deity is an ignorance to which the soul is everlastingly condemned." This our present ignorance ended, so far as Poe was concerned, on the stormy night of February third, 1848, when for two hours he read *Eureka* to a small but appreciative audience at the New York Society Library. (Putnam's later published it, giving him an advance of $14.) Displaying a wide acquaintance with physical science from Newton on, Poe attempted nothing less in *Eureka* than to explain the nature of the universe in terms of the intention of its Creator. That it fails is less surprising than the coherence of its general argument, the closeness of its reasoning, and the imaginative success of some of its parts. It is also surprising that such an intellectual performance was possible for Poe even in that terrible last period of psychological disintegration after the death of Virginia. "Man doth not yield himself to . . . death utterly, save only through the weakness of his feeble will."

Eureka is subtitled "A Prose Poem." It is much too long to be included here—but one passage may be quoted because it describes Poe's own literary method:

> In human constructions a particular cause has a particular effect; a particular intention brings to pass a particular object; but this is all; we see no reciprocity. The effect does not react upon the cause; the intention does not change relations with the object. In Divine constructions . . . we may take at any time a cause for an effect, or the converse—so that we can never absolutely decide which is which. . . .
>
> The pleasure that we derive from any display of human ingenuity is in the ratio of *the approach* to this species of reciprocity. In the construction of *plot*, for example, in fictitious literature, we should aim at so arranging the incidents that we shall not be able to determine, of any one of them, whether it depends from any other or upholds it. In this sense, of course, *perfection* of *plot* is really, or practically, unattainable—but only because it is a finite intelligence that constructs. The plots of God are perfect. The Universe is a plot of God.

In his poetry, Poe tried for a unity of means and ends, of technique and emotion, so that cause and effect become as interchangeable as certain physicists of our time have found them to be; or as they are in those perfect plots of God, where "we can never absolutely decide which is which." A seamless garment. "He believed, true poet that he was," Baudelaire says, "that the goal of poetry is of the same nature as its principle, and that it should have nothing in view but itself." In Mr. Eliot's paraphrase: " 'A poem does not say something—it *is* something': that doctrine has been held in more recent times." Or in Archibald MacLeish's: "A poem should not mean / But be." Or in Poe's words: "I would define poetry as The Rhythmical Creation of Beauty. Its sole arbiter is taste. With the Intellect or with the Conscience it has only collateral relations. Unless incidentally, it has no concern whatever with Duty or with Truth." So much for Keats' "Beauty is truth, truth beauty," or Wordsworth's *Ode to Duty*—"Stern daughter of the voice of God!" And so much for all the other nineteenth-century English poets, with one exception who—unlike the French symbolists—is ignored by the literary historians. The opening stanzas of his masterpiece are as musically "absolute" poetry as *Ulalume:*

> When awful darkness and silence reign
> Over the great Gromboolian plain,
>   Through the long wintry nights;
> When the angry breakers roar
> As they beat on the rocky shore;
>   When storm-clouds brood on the towering heights
> Of the hills of the Chankly Bore—
>
> Then through the vast and gloomy dark
> There moves what seems a fiery spark—
>   A lonely spark with silvery rays
>   Piercing the coal-black night,
>   A meteor strange and bright!
>   Hither and thither the vision strays,
>   A single lurid light.
>
> Slowly it wanders, pauses, creeps;
> Anon it sparkles, flashes and leaps;
> And ever as onward it gleaming goes
> A light on the Bong-tree stems it throws.
> And those who watch at that midnight hour
> From hall or terrace or lofty tower
> Cry, as the wild light passes along,
>   "The Dong! The Dong!
> The wandering Dong through the forest goes!
>   The Dong! The Dong!
> The Dong with a luminous nose!"

Whether Edward Lear was acquainted with Poe's verse—he read very little, in fact almost nothing—I don't know and, except for a passing remark by Mr. Eliot, whom little escaped, I've found no mention of Lear in Poe criticism. But to my ear, the so-called "nonsense" verses of Lear are full of echoes of Poe, of whom he seems to me a close relative, whether in the direct line (influenced by, school of . . .) or collateral (two minds reaching the same point, independently, like Baudelaire and Poe—or Darwin and Wallace). *The Dong with the Luminous Nose* cele-brates, in Poesque versification, a Poesque subject: the loss of the poet's one great love and his despairing quest for a past he knows will never return. In the case of the Dong, it was a Jumbly girl "who came to those shores one day" sailing in a sieve with her fellow Jumblies, as was their custom, and, after an interlude of innocent delight ("Happily, happily passed those days! / While the cheerful Jumblies staid . . . . / For day and night he was always there / By the side of the Jumbly girl so fair / With her sky-blue hands and her sea-green hair") sails away again, as was also the Jumbly custom.

> And the Dong was left on the cruel shore
> Gazing, gazing forevermore. . . .
> And now each night and all night long
> Over those plains still roams the Dong,
> And above the wail of the Chimp and the Snipe
> You may hear the wail of his plaintive pipe,
> While ever he seeks, but seeks in vain
> To meet with his Jumbly girl again.

More than one poem in this volume—once prejudices are overcome against "nonsense verse," which appears to me less nonsensical than it did to the Victorians—will be found to strike the same musical, and thematic, note as the above. It is not likely that Lear ever grappled with Poe's *Philosophy of Composition*, which explains precisely why "Nevermore!" with its long, open, mournful vowels was the only possible refrain for *The Raven*. But Lear's "gazing forevermore" follows Poe's rule, as, come to think of it, does the long, sad vowel sound, just what the mood requires, of "nose." That for cultural-psychological reasons too complex to go into here, of the chief features of the human face —brow, eyes, lips, mouth, nose—only the latter is a subject for humor, this is beside the present point, as are the blue hands and green hair of the Jumbly girl who was loved and lost by the Dong with the luminous nose. Or "nooowze."

Poe calculated his poems, at least in theory, as a general plans his campaigns, concentrating on strategy rather than tactics, on the main objective rather than on the skirmishes. Or as a good architect lays out a building, subordinating detail to general structure. In Baudelaire's words: "He has subjected inspiration to method, to the most severe analysis. 'Everything for the conclusion!' he often repeats. Even a sonnet needs a plan, and the construction, the armature, so to speak, is the most important guarantee of the mysterious life of works of the mind."

For Poe, this constructive armature was music. "It is in music," he writes, "that the soul most nearly attains the great end for which, when inspired by the Poetic Sentiment, it struggles—the creation of supernal beauty . . . . We are often made to feel, with a shivering delight, that from an earthly harp are stricken notes that *cannot* have been unfamiliar to the angels." The sentiment and the style grate on the contemporary ear: we don't believe in soul-struggles nor in angels nor in beauty even when it is not "supernal" (of which our suspicions are confirmed when we look it up and find it means "being in or belonging to the heaven of divine beings"). Harps, earthly or not, are suspect, "shivering delight" makes us shiver with undelight, and we are put off by Poe's weakness for capitalization and italics, excessive even for his time. Yet he meant it, and it has meaning. "I am profoundly excited by music," he wrote elsewhere—if only he had let it go at that! Few poets have been so preoccupied, analytically and creatively, with the musical aspects of verse. The only American poet of the last century to be so preoccupied was another Southerner, of the next generation, Sidney Lanier, whose life and personality in no way resembled Poe's, except that he, too, lived and died in poverty. Lanier was a practicing musician —he played the flute in the Baltimore Symphony—and his rhythmical experiments went far beyond Poe's, foreshadowing Gerard Manley Hopkins. Nothing of Poe's is as subtle or original—indeed, as good—as many passages in Lanier's verse—as, from *The Marshes of Glyn:*

> Sinuous southward and sinuous northward the shimmering band
> Of the sand-beach fastens the fringe of the marsh to the folds
> of the land.
> Inward and outward to northward and southward the beach-lines
> linger and curl

As a silver-wrought garment that clings to and follows the firm
        sweet limbs of a girl.
Vanishing, swerving, evermore curving again into sight,
Softly the sand-beach wavers away to a dim gray looping of light.

*   *   *

How still the plains of the waters be!
The tide is in his ecstasy.
The tide is at his greatest height:
    And it is night.

No, there is nothing on that level in Poe, from a technical
standpoint. And yet Poe is still considered, however grudgingly,
one of our major poets, while Lanier is not. It is most unfair.
"These trifles" of Poe continue to interest us, even to excite us
when we are young, while we merely admire Lanier's verse. I
think it is for the same reason that Poe instead of Coleridge inspired three generations of French symbolists: because of his
peculiar fusion of the particular and the general. He was "committed," in the modern sense, only to himself, to his own neuroses, prejudices, whims, tastes, and interests, but these were
enough. The fusion was so complete that some of his most casual
jottings have had great consequences. His note, "The orange
ray of the spectrum and the buzz of the gnats . . . affect me with
nearly similar sensations," led to Baudelaire's important sonnet,
Correspondances, and to Rimbaud's "interpenetration of the
senses," while the esthetic experiments of Des Esseintes, in
Huysmans' *A Rebours*, owe something to it, and to another note
in *Marginalia*: "I believe that odors have an altogether peculiar
force, in affecting us through association; a force differing *essentially* from that of objects addressing the touch, the taste, the
sight or the hearing."

If the clue to Poe's literary psyche is the will which dieth not,
I think the clue to the continuing interest of his poetry is this
combination of the personal and the impersonal, each carried to
an extreme, one playing against the other in a counterpoint that,
in the best of the poems—such as *Romance, Israfel, The City
in the Sea, The Sleeper, Dreamland, Ulalume,* and *For Annie*—
harmoniously contains a unity of opposites.

A Note on Selection and Arrangement:

The text I have used is that established by Killis Campbell in his definitive edition, The Poems of Edgar Allan Poe *(Boston, 1917; reissued New York, 1962) which gives the last text that Poe revised, generally that in the 1845 volume, and, in footnotes, all the earlier variants in the 1827, 1829, and 1831 volumes plus variants in the many magazine printings and reprintings in Poe's lifetime. Since Poe was an assiduous and ruthless reviser, you must go to Mr. Campbell's edition—which also has 217 pages of notes and biographical-historical Introduction, including a nineteen-page essay on "Poe's Passion for Revising His Poems"—if you want to see how Poe applied his theories to his practice.*

*Of the fifty-three poems Mr. Campbell prints as undoubtedly by Poe, I have chosen thirty-three, mostly because I liked them, a few chiefly for their biographical interest, and four (*Lenore, Eulalie, The Conqueror Worm, *and* The Raven) *because, although I think they present Poe at his most mechanical and melodramatic, they are too well known to omit. I have also used one of the ten poems Mr. Campbell gives as "attributed to Poe" on evidence he finds insufficient. If Poe didn't write* Alone, *he should have, for it is a concise definition of his poetic personality; as the Italian proverb goes,* se non è vero, è ben trovato— *if it isn't true, it ought to be.*

I have divided the poems into: I. "The Music of Things" (songs, lyrics, "pure" poetry); II. "Out of Time and Out of Space" (death and other worlds); III. "I Have Not Been as Others Were" (biographical).

These divisions shouldn't be taken too seriously. I have, for instance, put Ulalume *and the first* To Helen *under I because they seem predominantly pure music, and* For Annie *under II because its theme is death (this time the poet, not the lady, is dying). But they could also go under III, as could many others, for, as noted above, Poe was a most autobiographical poet.* To Helen *was inspired by the memory of his first "ideal love," the beautiful Mrs. Jane Stannard who was kind to him as a school-*

22

boy. For Annie *was written in 1849 for (and sent to) Mrs. Annie Richmond, of Lowell, Mass., one of the many sympathetic literary ladies he turned to after Virginia's death, but it is a strange love poem, concentrating on the lover and celebrating the beloved only as the bringer of surcease from "the fever called 'Living.'"* Even Ulalume, *his finest experiment in absolute music, may have a biographical clue. Written at the time of Virginia's death, the subject may be the poet's forgetting the dead Ulalume and trying to replace her with a new love, Psyche, and finally realizing the impossibility—and the horror—of the attempt as, at the end, they come to her tomb and he begins to remember ("Well I know, now, this dank tarn of Auber"). Which was precisely what did happen, more than once, in those desperate three years after Virginia's death. That Poe told a Miss Ingram the poem "was scarcely clear to himself" seems, if I may be Freudian for once, evidence in favor of this interpretation.*

The biographical poems in III are variations on a constant, an obsessive theme: past joy and innocence contrasted to present pain and knowledge—the expulsion from Eden. Alone *and* Israfel *state it in terms of the poet's vocation.* Romance, Dreams, The Lake, *and* A Dream within a Dream—*all of them early poems—picture the dreaming child (though a child "with a most knowing eye") who is later overwhelmed by "eternal Condor years"—surely a great simile—that "shake the very Heaven on high / With tumult as they thunder by." Poe's early loss of Sarah Royster to a socially superior rival—another expulsion from Eden—is the theme of* To One in Paradise *and* Bridal Ballad; *in* Lenore *it is intertwined with his other great early loss, to death, of Mrs. Stannard.* Eulalie, *which was written in 1845 just after the success of* The Raven, *when Poe was, according to Campbell, "in exceptionally high spirits" shows that cheerfulness may not have suited him; it is so bad that in my anthology,* Parodies from Chaucer to Beerbohm *(1960) I included it as a self-parody.* Eulalie *is Virginia, who is celebrated more successfully in the prose of* Eleanora, *written in 1842 when Poe's spirits were perhaps not so high.* Eleanora *is an idyll of* happiness in love, the very landscape suggesting Virginia's quiet domestic beauty: the Valley of the Many-Colored Grass, peaceful and remote, where "we lived all alone, knowing nothing of the world without. . . . I and my cousin and her mother." Eleanora dies and the narrator, though he had promised her never to remarry, leaves the valley and marries "the ethereal Ermengarde"; his dead love appears to him, but she is a gentle, forgiving spirit, not like the vengeful Morella, and she absolves him of his vows and bids him take Ermengarde to his heart and "sleep in peace." That Poe should have written this autobiographical parable in 1841, six years before Virginia's death, shows his obsession with the death of beloved and beautiful women. As prophecy, Ulalume was more accurate, for while Virginia's spirit was doubtless as gently forgiving as Eleanora's, his own morbid sense of guilt harassed him into self-destruction when he tried to forget his dead love by courting other women.

To Helen was written for Sarah Helen Whitman, a poetess who lived in Rhode Island, to whom he became engaged after Virginia's death—she broke it off when he didn't keep his promise to give up liquor. An Enigma is a jeu d'esprit tossed off for another poetess, Sarah Anne Lewis, of Baltimore; it is an acrostic spelling her name—first letter of the first line "S," second letter of second line "A," etc. There is a touching symmetry in the last two poems in this section, which were also the last written by Poe: Annabel Lee was for his dead wife ("I was a child and she was a child / In this kingdom by the sea") and To My Mother was for Mrs. Clemm. As if he knew his death was near and was settling his account with the two persons he had loved and trusted, paying them in the only currency he had and drawing a double line under the balance. The mother. The daughter. The wife. The sister. The brother. And the child.

(I have included a few things in I, II, and III that are typographically prose but which seem to me poetry, creating a mood by rhythm and repetition that differs from prose as incantation differs from exposition. Silence, for example, is pure, absolute poetry like Kubla Khan, from its first sentence (" 'Listen to me,' said the Demon, as he placed his hand upon my head.") to the last, which has the true poetic magic, unexpected and nonsensi-cal (better, unsensical) and obviously—after Poe has done it—the only way to end such a fantasy without anticlimax: "And the lynx, which dwelleth forever in the tomb, came out there-from, and lay down at the feet of the Demon, and looked him steadily in the face.")

Section IV is devoted to Poe's criticism of poetry. It begins with his famous how-to-do-it essay, The Philosophy of Composi-tion, which explains how he manufactured The Raven. There is some mystification here. If a poem could be written by following the sort of cookbook recipe Poe gives for arriving at "Never-more" as a refrain, then we could all be poets; I suspect he got the refrain first and then concocted a recipe rather than the other way round. Baudelaire, who understood Poe better than anyone, recognized the mystification but wasn't bothered by it: "After all, a little charlatanism is always permitted to genius, and is even proper to it. It is, like rouge on the cheeks of a beautiful woman, an additional stimulus to the mind." He also saw there was much more involved than charlatanism: "Here is a poet who claims that his poem was composed in accordance with his metaphysics. He was fond of repeating, he who had a mature originality, that originality is a matter of apprenticeship . . . . The accidental and the unintelligible were his two great enemies. Did he make himself, by a strange and amusing vanity, much less inspired than he naturally was? Did he diminish the spontaneous factor in himself in order to give will a larger share? I should be rather inclined to think so . . . . The lovers of a 'fine frenzy' will perhaps be revolted by these 'cynical' maxims, but . . . it will always be useful to show them what profit art can draw from deliberation, and to make worldly people realize how much labor is required by that object of luxury called poetry."*

The other essays in Section IV give Poe's theories about poetry and illustrate his method. The Marginalia at the end,

* For "worldly people" substitute, today, certain schools of con-temporary poetry, painting, and music that are often taken to be "advanced" because "the accidental and the unintelligible" are the madness in their method.

presenting some of his best ideas in a form as free as it is com-
pact, were contributed as "filler" paragraphs to a number of
magazines: The Southern Literary Messenger, Graham's, The
Democratic Review, The Opal, *and* Godey's Lady's Book.

For those who want to read more of Poe, and know more
about him, I would recommend, in addition to Arthur H. Quinn's
life and Killis Campbell's edition of the poems, Baudelaire on
Poe, *translated and edited by L. and F. E. Hyslop (Bald Eagle*
Press, 1952). The most scholarly edition of Poe's works, and by
far the most complete, is James A. Harrison's (Thomas Y. Cro-
well, 1902), whose seventeen volumes contain much hitherto
uncollected journalism—essays, fiction, criticism—plus a volume
of letters.

Three recent Poe anthologies, all cheap and good are: Philip
Van Doren Stern's The Portable Poe *(Viking), T. O. Mab-*
bott's in the Modern Library (Random House), and the one in
the American Century Series edited by Margaret Alterton
and Hardin Craig (Hill & Wang). Stern has 54 pages of Poe's
letters and the most literary criticism; Mabbott has the most
poems and tales, also 23 pages of interestingly opinionated
notes; Alterton-Craig has less Poe than the other two but makes
up for it, or doesn't, by a formidable "critical apparatus"—136
pages of introduction and 77 pages of notes. Adding R. P.
Blackmur's New American Library paperback edition of The Fall
of the House of Usher and Other Tales, *which includes* A. Gordon Pym *complete as well as an "Afterword" by the editor that*
is short and masterful, one finds that the contemporary student
or enthusiast of Poe can buy all the major writings, together
with a great deal of scholarly data and comment, for less than
$7. A tribute to our "paperback revolution." And to the vitality
of Poe's work, which keeps putting out green shoots in spite of
all the weeding and pruning by the gardeners of the literary
Establishment.

I. "THE MUSIC OF THINGS"

ELDORADO

Gaily bedight,
A gallant knight,
In sunshine and in shadow,
Had journeyed long,
Singing a song,
In search of Eldorado.

But he grew old—
This knight so bold—
And o'er his heart a shadow
Fell as he found
No spot of ground
That looked like Eldorado.

And, as his strength
Failed him at length,
He met a pilgrim shadow—
"Shadow," said he,
"Where can it be—
This land of Eldorado?"

"Over the Mountains
Of the Moon,
Down the Valley of the Shadow,
Ride, boldly ride,"
The shade replied,—
"If you seek for Eldorado!"

TO HELEN

Helen, thy beauty is to me
 Like those Nicéan barks of yore,
That gently, o'er a perfumed sea,
 The weary, way-worn wanderer bore
 To his own native shore.

On desperate seas long wont to roam,
 Thy hyacinth hair, thy classic face,
Thy Naiad airs have brought me home
 To the glory that was Greece
And the grandeur that was Rome.

Lo! in yon brilliant window-niche
 How statue-like I see thee stand,
 The agate lamp within thy hand!
Ah, Psyche, from the regions which
 Are Holy Land!

ULALUME—A BALLAD

The skies they were ashen and sober;
  The leaves they were crispéd and sere—
 The leaves they were withering and sere:
It was night, in the lonesome October
 Of my most immemorial year:
It was hard by the dim lake of Auber,
 In the misty mid region of Weir—
It was down by the dank tarn of Auber,
  In the ghoul-haunted woodland of Weir.

Here once, through an alley Titanic,
    Of cypress, I roamed with my Soul—
    Of cypress, with Psyche, my Soul.
These were days when my heart was volcanic
    As the scoriac rivers that roll—
    As the lavas that restlessly roll
Their sulphurous currents down Yaanek
    In the ultimate climes of the Pole—
That groan as they roll down Mount Yaanek
    In the realms of the Boreal Pole.

Our talk had been serious and sober,
    But our thoughts they were palsied and sere—
    Our memories were treacherous and sere;
For we knew not the month was October,
    And we marked not the night of the year
    (Ah, night of all nights in the year!)—
We noted not the dim lake of Auber
    (Though once we had journeyed down here)—
We remembered not the dank tarn of Auber,
    Nor the ghoul-haunted woodland of Weir.

And now, as the night was senescent
    And star-dials pointed to morn—
    As the star-dials hinted of morn—
At the end of our path a liquescent
    And nebulous lustre was born,
Out of which a miraculous crescent
    Arose with a duplicate horn—
Astarte's bediamonded crescent
    Distinct with its duplicate horn.

And I said: "She is warmer than Dian;
    She rolls through an ether of sighs—
    She revels in a region of sighs.
She has seen that the tears are not dry on
    These cheeks, where the worm never dies,

And has come past the stars of the Lion,
  To point us the path to the skies—
  To the Lethean peace of the skies—
Come up, in despite of the Lion,
  To shine on us with her bright eyes—
Come up through the lair of the Lion,
  With love in her luminous eyes."

But Psyche, uplifting her finger,
  Said: "Sadly this star I mistrust—
  Her pallor I strangely mistrust:
Ah, hasten!—ah, let us not linger!
  Ah, fly!—let us fly!—for we must."
In terror she spoke, letting sink her
  Wings till they trailed in the dust—
In agony sobbed, letting sink her
  Plumes till they trailed in the dust—
  Till they sorrowfully trailed in the dust.

I replied: "This is nothing but dreaming:
  Let us on by this tremulous light!
  Let us bathe in this crystalline light!
Its Sibyllic splendor is beaming
  With Hope and in Beauty to-night:—
  See!—it flickers up the sky through the night!
Ah, we safely may trust to its gleaming,
  And be sure it will lead us aright—
We surely may trust to a gleaming,
  That cannot but guide us aright,
  Since it flickers up to Heaven through the night."

Thus I pacified Psyche and kissed her,
  And tempted her out of her gloom—
  And conquered her scruples and gloom;
And we passed to the end of the vista,
  But were stopped by the door of a tomb—
  By the door of a legended tomb;

And I said: "What is written, sweet sister,
  On the door of this legended tomb?"
  She replied: "Ulalume—Ulalume!—
  'Tis the vault of thy lost Ulalume!"

Then my heart it grew ashen and sober
  As the leaves that were crispéd and sere—
  As the leaves that were withering and sere;
And I cried: "It was surely October
  On *this* very night of last year
  That I journeyed—I journeyed down here!—
  That I brought a dread burden down here—
  On this night of all nights in the year,
  Ah, what demon hath tempted me here?
Well I know, now, this dim lake of Auber—
  This misty mid region of Weir—
Well I know, now, this dank tarn of Auber,
  This ghoul-haunted woodland of Weir."

Said we, then—the two, then: "Ah, can it
  Have been that the woodlandish ghouls—
  The pitiful, the merciful ghouls—
To bar up our way and to ban it
  From the secret that lies in these wolds—
  From the thing that lies hidden in these wolds—
Have drawn up the spectre of a planet
  From the limbo of lunary souls—
This sinfully scintillant planet
  From the Hell of the planetary souls?"

SONG FROM "AL AARAAF"

" 'Neath blue-bell or streamer—
　　Or tufted wild spray
That keeps from the dreamer
　　The moonbeam away—
Bright beings! that ponder,
　　With half closing eyes,
On the stars which your wonder
　　Hath drawn from the skies,
Till they glance thro' the shade, and
　　Come down to your brow
Like—eyes of the maiden
　　Who calls on you now—
Arise! from your dreaming
　　In violet bowers,
To duty beseeming
　　These star-litten hours—
And shake from your tresses,
　　Encumber'd with dew,
The breath of those kisses
　　That cumber them too
(O, how, without you, Love!
　　Could angels be blest?)—
Those kisses of true love
　　That lull'd ye to rest!
Up!—shake from your wing
　　Each hindering thing:
The dew of the night—
　　It would weigh down your flight;
And true love caresses—
　　O! leave them apart:
They are light on the tresses,
　　But lead on the heart.

"Ligeia! Ligeia!
    My beautiful one!
Whose harshest idea
    Will to melody run,
O! is it thy will
    On the breezes to toss?
Or, capriciously still,
    Like the lone Albatross,
Incumbent on night
    (As she on the air)
To keep watch with delight
    On the harmony there?

"Ligeia! wherever
    Thy image may be,
No magic shall sever
    Thy music from thee.
Thou hast bound many eyes
    In a dreamy sleep—
But the strains still arise
    Which *thy* vigilance keep:
The sound of the rain
    Which leaps down to the flower,
And dances again
    In the rhythm of the shower—
The murmur that springs
    From the growing of grass
Are the music of things—
    But are modell'd, alas!—
Away, then, my dearest,
    O! hie thee away
To springs that lie clearest
    Beneath the moon-ray—
To lone lake that smiles,

In its dream of deep rest,
    At the many star-isles
        That enjewel its breast—
Where wild flowers, creeping,
        Have mingled their shade,
On its margin is sleeping
        Full many a maid—
Some have left the cool glade, and
        Have slept with the bee—
Arouse them, my maiden,
        On moorland and lea—
Go! breathe on their slumber,
        All softly in ear,
The musical number
        They slumber'd to hear—
For what can awaken
        An angel so soon,
Whose sleep hath been taken
        Beneath the cold moon,
As the spell which no slumber
        Of witchery may test,
The rhythmical number
        Which lull'd him to rest?"

SILENCE

The mountain pinnacles slumber; valleys, crags and caves *are silent.*

ALCMAN. [60(10),646].

"LISTEN TO *me*," said the Demon, as he placed his hand upon my head. "The region of which I speak is a dreary region in Libya, by the borders of the river Zäire. And there is no quiet there, nor silence.

"The waters of the river have a saffron and sickly hue; and they flow not onwards to the sea, but palpitate forever and forever beneath the red eye of the sun with a tumultuous and convulsive motion. For many miles on either side of the river's oozy bed is a pale desert of gigantic water-lilies. They sigh one unto the other in that solitude, and stretch towards the heaven their long and ghastly necks, and nod to and fro their everlasting heads. And there is an indistinct murmur which cometh out from among them like the rushing of subterrene water. And they sigh one unto the other.

"But there is a boundary to their realm—the boundary of the dark, horrible, lofty forest. There, like the waves about the Hebrides, the low underwood is agitated continually. But there is no wind throughout the heaven. And the tall primeval trees rock eternally hither and thither with a crashing and mighty sound. And from their high summits, one by one, drop everlasting dews. And at the roots strange poisonous flowers lie writhing in perturbed slumber. And overhead, with a rustling and loud noise, the gray clouds rush westwardly forever, until they roll, a cataract, over the fiery wall of the horizon. But there is no wind throughout the heaven. And by the shores of the river Zäire there is neither quiet nor silence.

"It was night, and the rain fell; and, falling, it was rain, but, having fallen, it was blood. And I stood in the morass among the tall lilies, and the rain fell upon my head—and the lilies sighed one unto the other in the solemnity of their desolation.

"And, all at once, the moon arose through the thin ghastly mist, and was crimson in color. And mine eyes fell upon a huge

37

gray rock which stood by the shore of the river, and was lighted by the light of the moon. And the rock was gray, and ghastly, and tall,—and the rock was gray. Upon its front were characters engraven in the stone; and I walked through the morass of water-lilies, until I came close unto the shore, that I might read the characters upon the stone. But I could not decypher them. And I was going back into the morass, when the moon shone with a fuller red, and I turned and looked again upon the rock, and upon the characters;—and the characters were DESOLATION.

"And I looked upwards, and there stood a man upon the summit of the rock; and I hid myself among the water-lilies that I might discover the actions of the man. And the man was tall and stately in form, and was wrapped up from his shoulders to his feet in the toga of old Rome. And the outlines of his figure were indistinct—but his features were the features of a deity; for the mantle of the night, and of the mist, and of the moon, and of the dew, had left uncovered the features of his face. And his brow was lofty with thought, and his eye wild with care; and, in the few furrows upon his cheek I read the fables of sorrow, and weariness, and disgust with mankind, and a longing after solitude.

"And the man sat upon the rock, and leaned his head upon his hand, and looked out upon the desolation. He looked down into the low unquiet shrubbery, and up into the tall primeval trees, and up higher at the rustling heaven, and into the crimson moon. And I lay close within shelter of the lilies, and observed the actions of the man. And the man trembled in the solitude;—but the night waned, and he sat upon the rock.

"And the man turned his attention from the heaven, and looked out upon the dreary river Zäire, and upon the yellow ghastly waters, and upon the pale legions of the water-lilies. And the man listened to the sighs of the water-lilies, and to the murmur that came up from among them. And I lay close within my covert and observed the actions of the man. And the man trembled in the solitude;—but the night waned and he sat upon the rock.

"Then I went down into the recesses of the morass, and

waded afar in among the wilderness of the lilies, and called unto the hippopotami which dwelt among the fens in the recesses of the morass. And the hippopotami heard my call, and came, with the behemoth, unto the foot of the rock, and roared loudly and fearfully beneath the moon. And I lay close within my covert and observed the actions of the man. And the man trembled in the solitude;—but the night waned and he sat upon the rock.

"Then I cursed the elements with the curse of tumult; and a frightful tempest gathered in the heaven where, before, there had been no wind. And the heaven became livid with the violence of the tempest—and the rain beat upon the head of the man—and the floods of the river came down—and the river was tormented into foam—and the water-lilies shrieked within their beds—and the forest crumbled before the wind—and the thunder rolled—and the lightning fell—and the rock rocked to its foundation. And I lay close within my covert and observed the actions of the man. And the man trembled in the solitude;— but the night waned and he sat upon the rock.

"Then I grew angry and cursed, with the curse of *silence*, the river, and the lilies, and the wind, and the forest, and the heaven, and the thunder, and the sighs of the water-lilies. And they became accursed, and *were still*. And the moon ceased to totter up its pathway to heaven—and the thunder died away—and the lightning did not flash—and the clouds hung motionless—and the waters sunk to their level and remained—and the trees ceased to rock—and the water-lilies sighed no more—and the murmur was heard no longer from among them, nor any shadow of sound throughout the vast illimitable desert. And I looked upon the characters of the rock, and they were changed;—and the characters were SILENCE.

"And mine eyes fell upon the countenance of the man, and his countenance was wan with terror. And, hurriedly, he raised his head from his hand, and stood forth upon the rock and listened. But there was no voice throughout the vast illimitable desert, and the characters upon the rock were SILENCE. And the man shuddered, and turned his face away, and fled afar off, in haste, so that I beheld him no more."

Now there are fine tales in the volumes of the Magi—in the iron-bound, melancholy volumes of the Magi. Therein, I say, are glorious histories of the Heaven, and of the Earth, and of the mighty sea—and of the Genii that over-ruled the sea, and the earth, and the lofty heaven. There was much lore too in the sayings which were said by the Sybils; and holy, holy things were heard of old by the dim leaves that trembled around Dodona—but, as Allah liveth, that fable which the Demon told me as he sat by my side in the shadow of the tomb, I hold to be the most wonderful of all! And as the Demon made an end of his story, he fell back within the cavity of the tomb and laughed. And I could not laugh with the Demon, and he cursed me because I could not laugh. And the lynx which dwelleth forever in the tomb, came out therefrom, and lay down at the feet of the Demon, and looked at him steadily in the face.

SONNET—TO SCIENCE

Science! true daughter of Old Time thou art!
    Who alterest all things with thy peering eyes.
Why preyest thou thus upon the poet's heart,
    Vulture, whose wings are dull realities?
How should he love thee? or how deem thee wise,
    Who wouldst not leave him in his wandering
To seek for treasure in the jewelled skies,
    Albeit he soared with an undaunted wing?
Hast thou not dragged Diana from her car,
    And driven the Hamadryad from the wood
To seek a shelter in some happier star?
    Hast thou not torn the Naiad from her flood,
The Elfin from the green grass, and from me
The summer dream beneath the tamarind tree?

LATIN HYMN

A thousand, a thousand, a thousand,
A thousand, a thousand, a thousand,
We, with one warrior, have slain!
A thousand, a thousand, a thousand, a thousand,
Sing a thousand over again!
Soho! Let us sing
Long life to our king,
Who knocked over a thousand so fine!
Soho! Let us roar,
He has given us more
Red gallons of gore
Than all Syria can furnish of wine!

SONG OF TRIUMPH

Who is king but Epiphanes?
Say—do you know?
Who is king but Epiphanes.
Bravo! Bravo!
There is none but Epiphanes,
No, there is none:
So tear down the temples,
And put out the sun!

THE COLISEUM

Type of the antique Rome! Rich reliquary
Of lofty contemplation left to Time
By buried centuries of pomp and power!
At length—at length—after so many days
Of weary pilgrimage and burning thirst
(Thirst for the springs of lore that in thee lie),
I kneel, an altered and an humble man,
Amid thy shadows, and so drink within
My very soul thy grandeur, gloom, and glory!

Vastness! and Age! and Memories of Eld!
Silence! and Desolation! and dim Night!
I feel ye now—I feel ye in your strength—
O spells more sure than e'er Judaean king
Taught in the gardens of Gethsemane!
O charms more potent than the rapt Chaldee
Ever drew down from out the quiet stars!

Here, where a hero fell, a column falls!
Here, where the mimic eagle glared in gold,
A midnight vigil holds the swarthy bat!
Here, where the dames of Rome their gilded hair
Waved to the wind, now wave the reed and thistle!
Here, where on golden throne the monarch lolled,
Glides, spectre-like, unto his marble home,
Lit by the wan light of the hornéd moon,
The swift and silent lizard of the stones!

But stay! these walls—these ivy-clad arcades—
These mouldering plinths—these sad and blackened shafts—
These vague entablatures—this crumbling frieze—
These shattered cornices—this wreck—this ruin—
These stones—alas! these gray stones—are they all—
All of the famed and the colossal left
By the corrosive Hours to Fate and me?

"Not all"—the Echoes answer me—"not all!
Prophetic sounds and loud, arise forever
From us, and from all Ruin, unto the wise,
As melody from Memnon to the Sun.
We rule the hearts of mightiest men—we rule
With a despotic sway all giant minds.
We are not impotent—we pallid stones.
Not all our power is gone—not all our fame—
Not all the magic of our high renown—
Not all the wonder that encircles us—
Not all the mysteries that in us lie—
Not all the memories that hang upon
And cling around about us as a garment,
Clothing us in a robe of more than glory."

THE BELLS

I.

Hear the sledges with the bells—
Silver bells!
What a world of merriment their melody foretells!
How they tinkle, tinkle, tinkle,
In the icy air of night!
While the stars that oversprinkle
All the heavens, seem to twinkle
With a crystalline delight;
Keeping time, time, time,
In a sort of Runic rhyme,
To the tintinnabulation that so musically wells
From the bells, bells, bells, bells,
Bells, bells, bells—
From the jingling and the tinkling of the bells.

II.

Hear the mellow wedding bells—
　　Golden bells!
What a world of happiness their harmony foretells!
　　Through the balmy air of night
　　How they ring out their delight!—
　　　From the molten-golden notes,
　　　　And all in tune,
　　　What a liquid ditty floats
To the turtle-dove that listens, while she gloats
　　　On the moon!
　　Oh, from out the sounding cells,
What a gush of euphony voluminously wells!
　　　　How it swells!
　　　　How it dwells
　　　On the Future!—how it tells
　　　Of the rapture that impels
　　To the swinging and the ringing
　　　Of the bells, bells, bells—
Of the bells, bells, bells, bells,
　　　Bells, bells, bells—
To the rhyming and the chiming of the bells!

III.

Hear the loud alarum bells—
　　Brazen bells!
What a tale of terror, now, their turbulency tells!
　　In the startled ear of night
　　How they scream out their affright!
　　Too much horrified to speak,
　　They can only shriek, shriek,
　　　Out of tune,
In a clamorous appealing to the mercy of the fire,
In a mad expostulation with the deaf and frantic fire,
　　Leaping higher, higher, higher,
　　With a desperate desire,

And a resolute endeavor
Now—now to sit, or never,
By the side of the pale-faced moon.
Oh, the bells, bells, bells!
What a tale their terror tells
Of Despair!
How they clang, and clash, and roar!
What a horror they outpour
On the bosom of the palpitating air!
Yet the ear, it fully knows,
By the twanging
And the clanging,
How the danger ebbs and flows;
Yet the ear distinctly tells,
In the jangling
And the wrangling,
How the danger sinks and swells,
By the sinking or the swelling in the anger of the bells—
Of the bells,—
Of the bells, bells, bells, bells,
Bells, bells, bells—
In the clamor and the clangor of the bells!

IV.

I Iear the tolling of the bells—
Iron bells!
What a world of solemn thought their monody compels!
In the silence of the night,
How we shiver with affright
At the melancholy menace of their tone!
For every sound that floats
From the rust within their throats
Is a groan.
And the people—ah, the people—
They that dwell up in the steeple,
All alone,

And who tolling, tolling, tolling,
    In that muffled monotone,
Feel a glory in so rolling
    On the human heart a stone—
They are neither man nor woman—
They are neither brute nor human—
        They are Ghouls:—
And their king it is who tolls:—
And he rolls, rolls, rolls,
        Rolls
    A paean from the bells!
And his merry bosom swells
    With the paean of the bells!
And he dances, and he yells;
Keeping time, time, time,
In a sort of Runic rhyme,
    To the paean of the bells—
        Of the bells:—
Keeping time, time, time,
In a sort of Runic rhyme,
    To the throbbing of the bells—
    Of the bells, bells, bells—
        To the sobbing of the bells;
    Keeping time, time, time,
        As he knells, knells, knells,
In a happy Runic rhyme,
        To the rolling of the bells—
    Of the bells, bells, bells:—
        To the tolling of the bells—
Of the bells, bells, bells, bells,
        Bells, bells, bells—
To the moaning and the groaning of the bells.

II. "OUT OF SPACE AND OUT OF TIME"

By a route obscure and lonely,
Haunted by ill angels only,
Where an Eidolon, named NIGHT,
On a black throne reigns upright,
I have reached these lands but newly
From an ultimate dim Thule—
From a wild weird clime that lieth, sublime,
Out of SPACE—out of TIME.

Bottomless vales and boundless floods,
And chasms, and caves, and Titan woods,
With forms that no man can discover
For the tears that drip all over;
Mountains toppling evermore
Into seas without a shore;
Seas that restlessly aspire,
Surging, unto skies of fire;
Lakes that endlessly outspread
Their lone waters, lone and dead,—
Their still waters, still and chilly
With the snows of the lolling lily.

By the lakes that thus outspread
Their lone waters, lone and dead,—
Their sad waters, sad and chilly
With the snows of the lolling lily,—
By the mountains—near the river
Murmuring lowly, murmuring ever,—
By the grey woods,—by the swamp
Where the toad and the newt encamp,—
By the dismal tarns and pools
    Where dwell the Ghouls,—
By each spot the most unholy—
In each nook most melancholy,—
There the traveller meets, aghast,

Sheeted Memories of the Past—
Shrouded forms that start and sigh
As they pass the wanderer by—
White-robed forms of friends long given,
In agony, to the Earth—and Heaven.

For the heart whose woes are legion
'T is a peaceful, soothing region—
For the spirit that walks in shadow
'T is—oh, 't is an Eldorado!
But the traveller, travelling through it,
May not—dare not openly view it;
Never its mysteries are exposed
To the weak human eye unclosed;
So wills its King, who hath forbid
The uplifting of the fringéd lid;
And thus the sad Soul that here passes
Beholds it but through darkened glasses.

By a route obscure and lonely,
Haunted by ill angels only,
Where an Eidolon, named NIGHT,
On a black throne reigns upright,
I have wandered home but newly
From this ultimate dim Thule.

THE CITY IN THE SEA

Lo! Death has reared himself a throne
In a strange city lying alone
Far down within the dim West,
Where the good and the bad and the worst and the best
Have gone to their eternal rest.
There shrines and palaces and towers
(Time-eaten towers that tremble not!)
Resemble nothing that is ours.
Around, by lifting winds forgot,
Resignedly beneath the sky
The melancholy waters lie.

No rays from the holy heaven come down
On the long night-time of that town;
But light from out the lurid sea
Streams up the turrets silently—
Gleams up the pinnacles far and free—
Up domes—up spires—up kingly halls—

Up fanes—up Babylon-like walls—
Up shadowy long-forgotten bowers
Of sculptured ivy and stone flowers—
Up many and many a marvellous shrine
Whose wreathéd friezes intertwine
The viol, the violet, and the vine.

Resignedly beneath the sky
The melancholy waters lie.
So bland the turrets and shadows there
That all seem pendulous in air,
While from a proud tower in the town
Death looks gigantically down.

There open fanes and gaping graves
Yawn level with the luminous waves;
But not the riches there that lie
In each idol's diamond eye—
Not the gaily-jewelled dead
Tempt the waters from their bed;
For no ripples curl, alas!
Along that wilderness of glass—
No swellings tell that winds may be
Upon some far-off happier sea—
No heavings hint that winds have been
On seas less hideously serene.

But lo, a stir is in the air!
The wave—there is a movement there!
As if the towers had thrust aside,
In slightly sinking, the dull tide—
As if their tops had feebly given
A void within the filmy Heaven.
The waves have now a redder glow—
The hours are breathing faint and low—
And when, amid no earthly moans,
Down, down that town shall settle hence,
Hell, rising from a thousand thrones,
Shall do it reverence.

THE SLEEPER

At midnight, in the month of June,
I stand beneath the mystic moon.
An opiate vapor, dewy, dim,
Exhales from out her golden rim,
And softly dripping, drop by drop,
Upon the quiet mountain top,
Steals drowsily and musically
Into the universal valley.
The rosemary nods upon the grave;
The lily lolls upon the wave;
Wrapping the fog about its breast,
The ruin moulders into rest;
Looking like Lethe, see! the lake
A conscious slumber seems to take,
And would not, for the world, awake.
All Beauty sleeps!—and lo! where lies
Irene, with her Destinies!

Oh, lady bright! can it be right—
This window open to the night?
The wanton airs, from the tree-top,
Laughingly through the lattice drop—
The bodiless airs, a wizard rout,
Flit through thy chamber in and out,
And wave the curtain canopy
So fitfully—so fearfully—
Above the closed and fringéd lid
'Neath which thy slumb'ring soul lies hid,
That, o'er the floor and down the wall,
Like ghosts the shadows rise and fall!
Oh, lady dear, hast thou no fear?
Why and what art thou dreaming here?
Sure thou art come o'er far-off seas,
A wonder to these garden trees!

Strange is thy pallor! strange thy dress!
Strange, above all, thy length of tress,
And this all solemn silentness!

The lady sleeps! Oh, may her sleep,
Which is enduring, so be deep!
Heaven have her in its sacred keep!
This chamber changed for one more holy,
This bed for one more melancholy,
I pray to God that she may lie
Forever with unopened eye,
While the pale sheeted ghosts go by!

My love, she sleeps! Oh, may her sleep,
As it is lasting, so be deep!
Soft may the worms about her creep!
Far in the forest, dim and old,
For her may some tall vault unfold—
Some vault that oft hath flung its black
And wingéd pannels fluttering back,
Triumphant, o'er the crested palls
Of her grand family funerals—

Some sepulchre, remote, alone,
Against whose portal she hath thrown,
In childhood, many an idle stone—
Some tomb from out whose sounding door
She ne'er shall force an echo more,
Thrilling to think, poor child of sin!
It was the dead who groaned within.

THE NARRATIVE OF A. GORDON PYM (*excerpt*)

Editor's Note: I reproduce below the last page of this novel because I think it is one of Poe's supreme efforts of poetical imagination. The narrator, Pym, accompanied by his shipmate, Peters, and Nu-Nu, whom they have abducted from the Antarctic island of Tsalal (where all is black, from the volcanic rocks to the skin and even the teeth of the natives, who are terrified by anything white such as a handkerchief or a sail) is rapidly drifting southward in a small boat "under the influence of a powerful current"—i.e., toward the South Pole, which was, of course, in 1838 still terra incognita. *The problem of resolving the supernatural without falling into either unconvincing vagueness or realistic anticlimax I think has been handled superbly,* pace *Henry James, whose contrary opinion must be respected because of* The Turn of the Screw.

March 8th.—To-day there floated by us one of the white animals whose appearance upon the beach at Tsalal had occasioned so wild a commotion among the savages. I would have picked it up, but there came over me a sudden listlessness, and I forbore. The heat of the water still increased, and the hand could no longer be endured within it. Peters spoke little, and I knew not what to think of his apathy. Nu-Nu breathed, and no more.

March 9th.—The whole ashy material fell now continually around us, and in vast quantities. The range of vapor to the southward had arisen prodigiously in the horizon, and began to assume more distinctness of form. I can liken it to nothing but a limitless cataract, rolling silently into the sea from some immense and far-distant rampart in the heaven. The gigantic curtain ranged along the whole extent of the southern horizon. It emitted no sound.

March 21st.—A sullen darkness now hovered above us—but from out the milky depths of the ocean a luminous glare arose, and stole up along the bulwarks of the boat. We were nearly overwhelmed by the white ashy shower which settled upon us and upon the canoe, but melted into the water as it fell. The summit of the cataract was utterly lost in the dimness and the distance. Yet we were evidently approaching it with a hideous velocity. At intervals there were visible in it wide, yawning, but momentary rents, and from out these rents, within which was a chaos of flitting and indistinct images, there came rushing and mighty, but soundless winds, tearing up the enkindled ocean in their course.

March 22d.—The darkness had materially increased, relieved only by the glare of the water thrown back from the white curtain before us. Many gigantic and pallidly white birds flew continuously now from beyond the veil, and their scream was the eternal *Tekeli-li!* as they retreated from our vision. Hereupon Nu-Nu stirred in the bottom of the boat; but upon touching him, we found his spirit departed. And now we rushed into the embraces of the cataract, where a chasm threw itself open to receive us. But there arose in our pathway a shrouded human figure, very far larger in its proportions than any dweller among men. And the hue of the skin of the figure was of the perfect whiteness of the snow.

SONNET—SILENCE

There are some qualities—some incorporate things,
    That have a double life, which thus is made
A type of that twin entity which springs
    From matter and light, evinced in solid and shade.
There is a two-fold *Silence*—sea and shore—
    Body and soul. One dwells in lonely places,
    Newly with grass o'ergrown; some solemn graces,
Some human memories and tearful lore,
Render him terrorless: his name's "No More."
He is the corporate Silence: dread him not!
    No power hath he of evil in himself;
But should some urgent fate (untimely lot!)
    Bring thee to meet his shadow (nameless elf,
That haunteth the lone regions where hath trod
No foot of man), commend thyself to God!

FAIRY-LAND

Dim vales—and shadowy floods—
And cloudy-looking woods,
Whose forms we can't discover
For the tears that drip all over.
Huge moons there wax and wane—
Again—again—again—
Every moment of the night—
Forever changing places—
And they put out the star-light
With the breath from their pale faces.
About twelve by the moon-dial
One more filmy than the rest
(A kind which, upon trial,
They have found to be the best)

Comes down—still down—and down
With its centre on the crown
Of a mountain's eminence,
While its wide circumference
In easy drapery falls
Over hamlets, over halls,
Wherever they may be—
O'er the strange woods—o'er the sea—
Over spirits on the wing—
Over every drowsy thing—
And buries them up quite
In a labyrinth of light—
And then, how deep!—O, deep!
Is the passion of their sleep.
In the morning they arise,
And their moony covering
Is soaring in the skies,
With the tempests as they toss,
Like——almost any thing—
Or a yellow Albatross.
They use that moon no more
For the same end as before—
Videlicet a tent—
Which I think extravagant:
Its atomies, however,
Into a shower dissever,
Of which those butterflies,
Of Earth, who seek the skies,
And so come down again
(Never-contented things!)
Have brought a specimen
Upon their quivering wings.

THE HAUNTED PALACE

In the greenest of our valleys
  By good angels tenanted,
Once a fair and stately palace—
  Radiant palace—reared its head.
In the monarch Thought's dominion,
  It stood there!
Never seraph spread a pinion
  Over fabric half so fair!

Banners yellow, glorious, golden,
  On its roof did float and flow
(This—all this—was in the olden
  Time long ago),
And every gentle air that dallied,
  In that sweet day,
Along the ramparts plumed and pallid,
  A wingéd odor went away.

Wanderers in that happy valley,
  Through two luminous windows, saw
Spirits moving musically,
  To a lute's well-tunéd law,
Round about a throne where, sitting,
  Porphyrogene!
In state his glory well befitting,
  The ruler of the realm was seen.

And all with pearl and ruby glowing
  Was the fair palace door,
Through which came flowing, flowing, flowing,
  And sparkling evermore,
A troop of Echoes, whose sweet duty
  Was but to sing,
In voices of surpassing beauty,
  The wit and wisdom of their king.

But evil things, in robes of sorrow,
　Assailed the monarch's high estate.
(Ah, let us mourn!—for never morrow
　Shall dawn upon him, desolate!)
And round about his home the glory
　That blushed and bloomed,
Is but a dim-remembered story
　Of the old time entombed.

And travellers, now, within that valley,
　Through the red-litten windows see
Vast forms that move fantastically
　To a discordant melody,
While, like a ghastly rapid river,
　Through the pale door
A hideous throng rush out forever,
　And laugh—but smile no more.

THE VALLEY OF UNREST

Once it smiled a silent dell
Where the people did not dwell;
They had gone unto the wars
Trusting to the mild-eyed stars,
Nightly, from their azure towers,
To keep watch above the flowers,
In the midst of which all day
The red sun-light lazily lay.
Now each visiter shall confess
The sad valley's restlessness.
Nothing there is motionless—
Nothing save the airs that brood
Over the magic solitude.
Ah, by no wind are stirred those trees
That palpitate like the chill seas
Around the misty Hebrides!
Ah, by no wind those clouds are driven
That rustle through the unquiet Heaven
Uneasily, from morn till even,
Over the violets there that lie
In myriad types of the human eye—
Over the lilies there that wave
And weep above a nameless grave!
They wave:—from out their fragrant tops
Eternal dews come down in drops.
They weep:—from off their delicate stems
Perennial tears descend in gems.

Yea! though I walk through the valley of the *Shadow:*
—*Psalm of David* [xxiii].

YE who read are still among the living: but I who write shall
have long since gone my way into the region of shadows. For
indeed strange things shall happen, and secret things be known,
and many centuries shall pass away, ere these memorials be seen
of men. And, when seen, there will be some to disbelieve, and
some to doubt, and yet a few who will find much to ponder
upon in the characters here graven with a stylus of iron.

The year had been a year of terror, and of feelings more intense than terror for which there is no name upon the earth. For
many prodigies and signs had taken place, and far and wide,
over sea and land, the black wings of the Pestilence were spread
abroad. To those, nevertheless, cunning in the stars, it was not
unknown that the heavens wore an aspect of ill; and to me,
the Greek Oinos, among others, it was evident that now had
arrived the alternation of that seven hundred and ninety-fourth
year when, at the entrance of Aries, the planet Jupiter is con-
joined with the red ring of the terrible Saturnus. The peculiar
spirit of the skies, if I mistake not greatly, made itself manifest,
not only in the physical orb of the earth, but in the souls, imag-
inations, and meditations of mankind.

Over some flasks of the red Chian wine, within the walls of a
noble hall, in a dim city called Ptolemais, we sat, at night, a
company of seven. And to our chamber there was no entrance
save by a lofty door of brass: and the door was fashioned by the
artizan Corinnos, and, being of rare workmanship, was fastened
from within. Black draperies, likewise, in the gloomy room, shut
out from our view the moon, the lurid stars, and the peopleless
streets—but the boding and the memory of Evil, they would
not be so excluded. There were things around us and about of
which I can render no distinct account—things material and
spiritual—heaviness in the atmosphere—a sense of suffocation—
anxiety—and, above all, that terrible state of existence which

the nervous experience when the senses are keenly living and awake, and meanwhile the powers of thought lie dormant. A dead weight hung upon us. It hung upon our limbs—upon the household furniture—upon the goblets from which we drank; and all things were depressed, and borne down thereby—all things save only the flames of the seven iron lamps which illumined our revel. Uprearing themselves in tall slender lines of light, they thus remained burning all pallid and motionless; and in the mirror which their lustre formed upon the round table of ebony at which we sat, each of us there assembled beheld the pallor of his own countenance, and the unquiet glare in the downcast eyes of his companions. Yet we laughed and were merry in our proper way—which was hysterical; and sang the songs of Anacreon—which are madness; and drank deeply—although the purple wine reminded us of blood. For there was yet another tenant of our chamber in the person of young Zoilus. Dead, and at full length he lay, enshrouded;—the genius and the demon of the scene. Alas! he bore no portion in our mirth, save that his countenance, distorted with the plague, and his eyes in which Death had but half extinguished the fire of the pestilence, seemed to take such interest in our merriment as the dead may haply take in the merriment of those who are to die. But although I, Oinos, felt that the eyes of the departed were upon me, still I forced myself not to perceive the bitterness of their expression, and, gazing down steadily into the depths of the ebony mirror, sang with a loud and sonorous voice the songs of the son of Teios. But gradually my songs they ceased, and their echoes, rolling afar off among the sable draperies of the chamber, became weak, and undistinguishable, and so faded away. And lo! from among those sable draperies where the sounds of the song departed, there came forth a dark and undefined shadow—a shadow such as the moon, when low in heaven, might fashion from the figure of a man: but it was the shadow neither of man, nor of God, nor of any familiar thing. And, quivering awhile among the draperies of the room, it at length rested in full view upon the surface of the door of brass. But the shadow was vague, and formless, and indefinite, and was the shadow neither of man, nor of God—neither God of Greece, nor God of Chaldaea, nor any Egyptian God. And the shadow rested upon the brazen doorway, and under the arch of the entablature of the door, and moved not, nor spoke any word, but there became stationary and remained. And the door whereupon the shadow rested was, if I remember aright, over against the feet of the young Zoilus enshrouded. But we, the seven there assembled, having seen the shadow as it came out from among the draperies, dared not steadily behold it, but cast down our eyes, and gazed continually into the depths of the mirror of ebony. And at length I, Oinos, speaking some low words, demanded of the shadow its dwelling and its appellation. And the shadow answered, "I am SHADOW, and my dwelling is near to the Catacombs of Ptolemais, and hard by those dim plains of Helusion which border upon the foul Charonian canal." And then did we, the seven, start from our seats in horror, and stand trembling, and shuddering, and aghast: for the tones in the voice of the shadow were not the tones of any one being, but of a multitude of beings, and, varying in their cadences from syllable to syllable, fell duskily upon our ears in the well remembered and familiar accents of many thousand departed friends.

THE CONQUEROR WORM

Lo! 't is a gala night
  Within the lonesome latter years!
And angel throng, bewinged, bedight
  In veils, and drowned in tears,
Sit in a theatre, to see
  A play of hopes and fears,
While the orchestra breathes fitfully
  The music of the spheres.

Mimes, in the form of God on high,
  Mutter and mumble low,
And hither and thither fly—
  Mere puppets they, who come and go
At bidding of vast formless things
  That shift the scenery to and fro,
Flapping from out their Condor wings
  Invisible Wo!

That motley drama—oh, be sure
  It shall not be forgot!
With its Phantom chased for evermore
  By a crowd that seize it not,
Through a circle that ever returneth in
  To the self-same spot,
And much of Madness, and more of Sin,
  And Horror the soul of the plot.

But see, amid the mimic rout,
  A crawling shape intrude
A blood-red thing that writhes from out
  The scenic solitude!
It writhes!—it writhes!—with mortal pangs
  The mimes become its food,
And seraphs sob at vermin fangs
  In human gore imbued.

Out—out are the lights—out all!
    And, over each quivering form,
The curtain, a funeral pall,
    Comes down with the rush of a storm,
While the angels, all pallid and wan,
    Uprising, unveiling, affirm
That the play is the tragedy, "Man,"
    And its hero, the Conqueror Worm.

FOR ANNIE

Thank Heaven! the crisis,
    The danger, is past,
And the lingering illness
    Is over at last—
And the fever called "Living"
    Is conquered at last.

Sadly, I know
    I am shorn of my strength,
And no muscle I move
    As I lie at full length—
But no matter!—I feel
    I am better at length.

And I rest so composedly,
    Now, in my bed,
That any beholder
    Might fancy me dead—
Might start at beholding me,
    Thinking me dead.

The moaning and groaning,
  The sighing and sobbing,
Are quieted now,
  With that horrible throbbing
At heart:—ah, that horrible,
  Horrible throbbing!

The sickness—the nausea—
  The pitiless pain—
Have ceased, with the fever
  That maddened my brain—
With the fever called "Living"
  That burned in my brain.

And oh! of all tortures
  That torture the worst
Has abated—the terrible
  Torture of thirst
For the naphthaline river
  Of Passion accurst:—
I have drank of a water
  That quenches all thirst:—

Of a water that flows,
  With a lullaby sound,
From a spring but a very few
  Feet under ground—
From a cavern not very far
  Down under ground.

And ah! let it never
  Be foolishly said
That my room it is gloomy
  And narrow my bed;
For man never slept
  In a different bed—

And, to *sleep*, you must slumber
  In just such a bed.

My tantalized spirit
  Here blandly reposes,
Forgetting, or never
  Regretting, its roses—
Its old agitations
  Of myrtles and roses:

For now, while so quietly
  Lying, it fancies
A holier odor
  About it, of pansies—
A rosemary odor,
  Commingled with pansies—
With rue and the beautiful
  Puritan pansies.

And so it lies happily,
  Bathing in many
A dream of the truth
  And the beauty of Annie—
Drowned in a bath
  Of the tresses of Annie.

She tenderly kissed me,
  She fondly caressed,
And then I fell gently
  To sleep on her breast—
Deeply to sleep
  From the heaven of her breast.

When the light was extinguished,
  She covered me warm,
And she prayed to the angels
  To keep me from harm—

To the queen of the angels
  To shield me from harm.

And I lie so composedly,
  Now, in my bed
(Knowing her love),
  That you fancy me dead—
And I rest so contentedly,
  Now, in my bed
(With her love at my breast),
  That you fancy me dead—
That you shudder to look at me,
  Thinking me dead:—

But my heart it is brighter
  Than all of the many
Stars in the sky,
  For it sparkles with Annie—
It glows with the light
  Of the love of my Annie—
With the thought of the light
  Of the eyes of my Annie.

THE CONVERSATION OF EIROS AND CHARMION

I will bring fire to thee.—EURIPIDES, *Androm.* [257].

EIROS

WHY do you call me Eiros?

CHARMION

So henceforward will you always be called. You must forget, too, *my* earthly name, and speak to me as Charmion.

EIROS

This is indeed no dream!

CHARMION

Dreams are with us no more;—but of these mysteries anon. I rejoice to see you looking life-like and rational. The film of the shadow has already passed from off your eyes. Be of heart, and fear nothing. Your allotted days of stupor have expired, and, to-morrow, I will myself induct you into the full joys and wonders of your novel existence.

EIROS

True—I feel no stupor—none at all. The wild sickness and the terrible darkness have left me, and I hear no longer that mad, rushing, horrible sound, like the "voice of many waters." Yet my senses are bewildered, Charmion, with the keenness of their perception of *the new*.

CHARMION

A few days will remove all this;—but I fully understand you, and feel for you. It is now ten earthly years since I underwent what you undergo—yet the remembrance of it hangs by me still. You have now suffered all of pain, however, which you will suffer in Aidenn.

In Aidenn?

In Aidenn.

Oh God!—pity me, Charmion!—I am over-burthened with the majesty of all things—of the unknown now known—of the speculative Future merged in the august and certain Present.

Grapple not now with such thoughts. To-morrow we will speak of this. Your mind wavers, and its agitation will find relief in the exercise of simple memories. Look not around, nor forward—but back. I am burning with anxiety to hear the details of that stupendous event which threw you among us. Tell me of it. Let us converse of familiar things, in the old familiar language of the world which has so fearfully perished.

Most fearfully, fearfully!—this is indeed no dream.

Dreams are no more. Was I much mourned, my Eiros?

Mourned, Charmion?—oh deeply. To that last hour of all, there hung a cloud of intense gloom and devout sorrow over your household.

And that last hour—speak of it. Remember that, beyond the naked fact of the catastrophe itself, I know nothing. When, coming out from among mankind, I passed into Night through the Grave—at that period, if I remember aright, the calamity which overwhelmed you was utterly unanticipated. But, indeed, I knew little of the speculative philosophy of the day.

EIROS

The individual calamity was, as you say, entirely unanticipated; but analogous misfortunes had been long a subject of discussion with astronomers. I need scarce tell you, my friend, that, even when you left us, men had agreed to understand those passages in the most holy writings which speak of the final destruction of all things by fire, as having reference to the orb of the earth alone. But in regard to the immediate agency of the ruin, speculation had been at fault from that epoch in astronomical knowledge in which the comets were divested of the terrors of flame. The very moderate density of these bodies had been well established. They had been observed to pass among the satellites of Jupiter, without bringing about any sensible alteration either in the masses or in the orbits of these secondary planets. We had long regarded the wanderers as vapory creations of inconceivable tenuity, and as altogether incapable of doing injury to our substantial globe, even in the event of contact. But contact was not in any degree dreaded; for the elements of all the comets were accurately known. That among *them* we should look for the agency of the threatened fiery destruction had been for many years considered an inadmissible idea. But wonders and wild fancies had been, of late days, strangely rife among mankind; and, although it was only with a few of the ignorant that actual apprehension prevailed, upon the announcement by astronomers of a *new* comet, yet this announcement was generally received with I know not what of agitation and mistrust.

The elements of the strange orb were immediately calculated, and it was at once conceded by all observers, that its path, at perihelion, would bring it into very close promixity with the earth. There were two or three astronomers, of secondary note,

72

who resolutely maintained that a contact was inevitable. I cannot very well express to you the effect of this intelligence upon the people. For a few short days they would not believe an assertion which their intellect, so long employed among worldly considerations, could not in any manner grasp. But the truth of a vitally important fact soon makes its way into the understanding of even the most stolid. Finally, all men saw that astronomical knowledge lied not, and they awaited the comet. Its approach was not, at first, seemingly rapid; nor was its appearance of very unusual character, it was a dull red, and had little perceptible train. For seven or eight days we saw no material increase in its apparent diameter, and but a partial alteration in its color. Meantime, the ordinary affairs of men were discarded, and all interests absorbed in a growing discussion, instituted by the philosophic, in respect to the cometary nature. Even the grossly ignorant aroused their sluggish capacities to such considerations. The learned *now* gave their intellect —their soul—to no such points as the allaying of fear, or to the sustenance of loved theory. They sought—they panted for right views. They groaned for perfected knowledge. *Truth* arose in the purity of her strength and exceeding majesty, and the wise bowed down and adored.

That material injury to our globe or to its inhabitants would result from the apprehended contact, was an opinion which hourly lost ground among the wise; and the wise were now freely permitted to rule the reason and the fancy of the crowd. It was demonstrated, that the density of the comet's *nucleus* was far less than that of our rarest gas; and the harmless passage of a similar visitor among the satellites of Jupiter was a point strongly insisted upon, and which served greatly to allay terror. Theologists, with an earnestness fear-enkindled, dwelt upon the biblical prophecies, and expounded them to the people with a directness and simplicity of which no previous instance had been known. That the final destruction of the earth must be brought about by the agency of fire, was urged with a spirit that enforced everywhere conviction; and that the comets were of no fiery nature (as all men now knew) was a truth which relieved all, in a great measure, from the apprehension of the great calamity foretold. It is noticeable that the popular prejudices and vulgar errors in regard to pestilence and wars—errors which were wont to prevail upon every appearance of a comet—were now altogether unknown. As if by some sudden convulsive exertion, reason had at once hurled superstition from her throne. The feeblest intellect had derived vigor from excessive interest.

What minor evils might arise from the contact were points of elaborate question. The learned spoke of slight geological disturbances, of probable alterations in climate, and consequently in vegetation; of possible magnetic and electric influences. Many held that no visible or perceptible effect would in any manner be produced. While such discussions were going on, their subject gradually approached, growing larger in apparent diameter, and of a more brilliant lustre. Mankind grew paler as it came. All human operations were suspended.

There was an epoch in the course of the general sentiment when the comet had attained, at length, a size surpassing that of any previously recorded visitation. The people now, dismissing any lingering hope that the astronomers were wrong, experienced all the certainty of evil. The chimerical aspect of their terror was gone. The hearts of the stoutest of our race beat violently within their bosoms. A very few days sufficed, however, to merge even such feelings in sentiments more unendurable. We could no longer apply to the strange orb any *accustomed* thoughts. Its *historical* attributes had disappeared. It oppressed us with a hideous *novelty* of emotion. We saw it not as an astronomical phenomenon in the heavens, but as an incubus upon our hearts, and a shadow upon our brains. It had taken, with inconceivable rapidity, the character of a gigantic mantle of rare flame, extending from horizon to horizon.

Yet a day, and men breathed with greater freedom. It was clear that we were already within the influence of the comet; yet we lived. We even felt an unusual elasticity of frame and vivacity of mind. The exceeding tenuity of the object of our dread was apparent; for all heavenly objects were plainly visible through it. Meantime, our vegetation had perceptibly altered;

and we gained faith, from this predicted circumstance, in the foresight of the wise. A wild luxuriance of foliage, utterly unknown before, burst upon every vegetable thing.

Yet another day—and the evil was not altogether upon us. It was now evident that its nucleus would first reach us. A wild change had come over all men; and the first sense of *pain* was the wild signal for general lamentation and horror. This first sense of pain lay in a rigorous constriction of the breast and lungs, and an insufferable dryness of the skin. It could not be denied that our atmosphere was radically affected; the conformation of this atmosphere and the possible modifications to which it might be subjected, were now the topics of discussion. The result of investigation sent an electric thrill of the intensest terror through the universal heart of man.

It had been long known that the air which encircled us was a compound of oxygen and nitrogen gases, in the proportion of twenty-one measures of oxygen, and seventy-nine of nitrogen, in every one hundred of the atmosphere. Oxygen, which was the principle of combustion, and the vehicle of heat, was absolutely necessary to the support of animal life, and was the most powerful and energetic agent in nature. Nitrogen, on the contrary, was incapable of supporting either animal life or flame. An unnatural excess of oxygen would result, it had been ascertained, in just such an elevation of the animal spirits as we had latterly experienced. It was the pursuit, the extension of the idea, which had engendered awe. What would be the result of a total extraction of the nitrogen? A combustion irresistible, all-devouring, omni-prevalent, immediate;—the entire fulfilment, in all their minute and terrible details, of the fiery and horror-inspiring, denunciations of the prophecies of the Holy Book.

Why need I paint, Charmion, the now disenchained frenzy of mankind? That tenuity in the comet which had previously inspired us with hope, was now the source of the bitterness of despair. In its impalpable gaseous character we clearly perceived the consummation of Fate. Meantime a day again passed—bearing away with it the last shadow of Hope. We gasped in the rapid modification of the air. The red blood bounded tumultuously through its strict channels. A furious delirium possessed all men; and, with arms rigidly outstretched towards the threatening heavens, they trembled and shrieked aloud. But the nucleus of the destroyer was now upon us;—even here in Aidenn, I shudder while I speak. Let me be brief—brief as the ruin that overwhelmed. For a moment there was a wild lurid light alone, visiting and penetrating all things. Then let us bow down, Charmion, before the excessive majesty of the great God—then, there came a shouting and pervading sound, as if from the mouth itself of HIM; while the whole incumbent mass of ether in which we existed, burst at once into a species of intense flame, for whose surpassing brilliancy and all-fervid heat even the angels in the high Heaven of pure knowledge have no name. Thus ended all.

Once upon a midnight dreary, while I pondered, weak and weary,
Over many a quaint and curious volume of forgotten lore—
While I nodded, nearly napping, suddenly there came a tapping,
As of some one gently rapping, rapping at my chamber door.
" 'T is some visitor," I muttered, "tapping at my chamber door—
 Only this and nothing more."

Ah, distinctly I remember it was in the bleak December;
And each separate dying ember wrought its ghost upon the floor.
Eagerly I wished the morrow;—vainly I had sought to borrow
From my books surcease of sorrow—sorrow for the lost Lenore—
For the rare and radiant maiden whom the angels name Lenore—
 Nameless *here* for evermore.

And the silken, sad, uncertain rustling of each purple curtain
Thrilled me—filled me with fantastic terrors never felt before;
So that now, to still the beating of my heart, I stood repeating,
" 'T is some visitor entreating entrance at my chamber door—
Some late visitor entreating entrance at my chamber door;—
 This it is and nothing more."

Presently my soul grew stronger; hesitating then no longer,
"Sir," said I, "or Madam, truly your forgiveness I implore;
But the fact is I was napping, and so gently you came rapping,
And so faintly you came tapping, tapping at my chamber door,
That I scarce was sure I heard you"—here I opened wide the
 door;—
 Darkness there and nothing more.

Deep into that darkness peering, long I stood there wondering,
 fearing,
Doubting, dreaming dreams no mortal ever dared to dream
 before;
But the silence was unbroken, and the stillness gave no token,

And the only word there spoken was the whispered word,
      "Lenore?"
This I whispered, and an echo murmured back the word,
      "Lenore!"
      Merely this and nothing more.

Back into the chamber turning, all my soul within me burning,
Soon again I heard a tapping somewhat louder than before.
"Surely," said I, "surely that is something at my window lattice;
Let me see, then, what thereat is, and this mystery explore—
Let my heart be still a moment and this mystery explore;—
      'T is the wind and nothing more!"

Open here I flung the shutter, when, with many a flirt and flutter,
In there stepped a stately Raven of the saintly days of yore;
Not the least obeisance made he; not a minute stopped or stayed
      he;
But, with mien of lord or lady, perched above my chamber door—
Perched upon a bust of Pallas just above my chamber door—
      Perched, and sat, and nothing more.

Then this ebony bird beguiling my sad fancy into smiling,
By the grave and stern decorum of the countenance it wore,
"Though thy crest be shorn and shaven, thou," I said, "art sure
      no craven,
Ghastly grim and ancient Raven wandering from the Nightly
      shore—
Tell me what thy lordly name is on the Night's Plutonian shore!"
      Quoth the Raven, "Nevermore."

Much I marvelled this ungainly fowl to hear discourse so plainly,
Though its answer little meaning—little relevancy bore;
For we cannot help agreeing that no living human being
Ever yet was blessed with seeing bird above his chamber door—
Bird or beast upon the sculptured bust above his chamber door,
      With such name as "Nevermore."

But the Raven, sitting lonely on the placid bust, spoke only
That one word, as if his soul in that one word he did outpour.
Nothing farther then he uttered—not a feather then he fluttered—
Till I scarcely more than muttered, "Other friends have flown
        before—
On the morrow *he* will leave me, as my Hopes have flown
        before."
        Then the bird said, "Nevermore."

Startled at the stillness broken by reply so aptly spoken,
"Doubtless," said I, "what it utters is its only stock and store
Caught from some unhappy master whom unmerciful Disaster
Followed fast and followed faster till his songs one burden bore—
Till the dirges of his Hope that melancholy burden bore
        Of 'Never—nevermore.' "

But the Raven still beguiling my sad fancy into smiling,
Straight I wheeled a cushioned seat in front of bird and bust
        and door;
Then, upon the velvet sinking, I betook myself to linking
Fancy unto fancy, thinking what this ominous bird of yore—
What this grim, ungainly, ghastly, gaunt, and ominous bird of
        yore
        Meant in croaking "Nevermore."

This I sat engaged in guessing, but no syllable expressing
To the fowl whose fiery eyes now burned into my bosom's core;
This and more I sat divining, with my head at ease reclining
On the cushion's velvet lining that the lamp-light gloated o'er,
But whose velvet-violet lining with the lamp-light gloating o'er,
        She shall press, ah, nevermore!

Then, methought, the air grew denser, perfumed from an unseen
        censer
Swung by seraphim whose foot-falls tinkled on the tufted floor.
"Wretch," I cried, "thy God hath lent thee—by these angels he
        hath sent thee

Respite—respite and nepenthe from thy memories of Lenore;
Quaff, oh, quaff this kind nepenthe and forget this lost Lenore!"
            Quoth the Raven, "Nevermore."

"Prophet!" said I, "thing of evil!—prophet still, if bird or devil!—
Whether Tempter sent, or whether tempest tossed thee here
            ashore,
Desolate yet all undaunted, on this desert land enchanted—
On this home by Horror haunted—tell me truly, I implore—
Is there—*is* there balm in Gilead?—tell me—tell me, I implore!"
            Quoth the Raven, "Nevermore."

"Prophet!" said I, "thing of evil!—prophet still, if bird or devil!
By that Heaven that bends above us—by that God we both
            adore—
Tell this soul with sorrow laden if, within the distant Aidenn,
It shall clasp a sainted maiden whom the angels name Lenore—
Clasp a rare and radiant maiden whom the angels name Lenore."
            Quoth the Raven, "Nevermore."

"Be that word our sign of parting, bird or fiend!" I shrieked,
            upstarting—
"Get thee back into the tempest and the Night's Plutonian shore!
Leave no black plume as a token of that lie thy soul hath spoken!
Leave my loneliness unbroken!—quit the bust above my door!
Take thy beak from out my heart, and take thy form from off
            my door!"
            Quoth the Raven, "Nevermore."

And the Raven, never flitting, still is sitting, *still* is sitting
On the pallid bust of Pallas just above my chamber door;
And his eyes have all the seeming of a demon's that is dreaming,
And the lamp-light o'er him streaming throws his shadow on
            the floor;
And my soul from out that shadow that lies floating on the floor
            Shall be lifted—nevermore!

III. "I HAVE NOT BEEN AS OTHERS WERE"

From childhood's hour I have not been
As others were—I have not seen
As others saw—I could not bring
My passions from a common spring—
From the same source I have not taken
My sorrow—I could not awaken
My heart to joy at the same tone—
And all I loved—*I* loved alone—
Then—in my childhood, in the dawn
Of a most stormy life—was drawn
From every depth of good and ill
The mystery which binds me still—
From the torrent, or the fountain—
From the red cliff of the mountain—
From the sun that round me rolled
In its autumn tint of gold—
From the lightning in the sky
As it pass'd me flying by—
From the thunder and the storm—
And the cloud that took the form
When the rest of Heaven was blue
Of a demon in my view.

ISRAFEL

And the angel Israfel, whose heart-strings are a lute, and who has the sweetest voice of all God's creatures.—KORAN.

In Heaven a spirit doth dwell
  "Whose heart-strings are a lute";
None sing so wildly well
As the angel Israfel,
And the giddy stars (so legends tell),
Ceasing their hymns, attend the spell
  Of his voice, all mute.

Tottering above
  In her highest noon,
  The enamoured moon
Blushes with love,
  While, to listen, the red levin
  (With the rapid Pleiads, even,
  Which were seven,)
  Pauses in Heaven.

And they say (the starry choir
  And the other listening things)
That Israfeli's fire
Is owing to that lyre
  By which he sits and sings—
The trembling living wire
  Of those unusual strings.

But the skies that angel trod,
  Where deep thoughts are a duty,
Where Love's a grown-up God,
  Where the Houri glances are
Imbued with all the beauty
  Which we worship in a star.

Therefore, thou art not wrong,
  Israfeli, who despisest
An unimpassioned song;
To thee the laurels belong,
  Best bard, because the wisest!
Merrily live, and long!

The ecstasies above
  With thy burning measures suit—
Thy grief, thy joy, thy hate, thy love,
  With the fervour of thy lute—
  Well may the stars be mute!

Yes, Heaven is thine; but this
  Is a world of sweets and sours,
  Our flowers are merely—flowers,
And the shadow of thy perfect bliss
  Is the sunshine of ours.

If I could dwell
Where Israfel
  Hath dwelt, and he where I,
He might not sing so wildly well
  A mortal melody,
While a bolder note than this might swell
  From my lyre within the sky.

DREAMS

Oh! that my young life were a lasting dream!
My spirit not awak'ning till the beam
Of an Eternity should bring the morrow.
Yes! tho' that long dream were of hopeless sorrow,
'T were better than the cold reality
Of waking life, to him whose heart must be,
And hath been still, upon the lovely earth,
A chaos of deep passion, from his birth.
But should it be—that dream eternally
Continuing—as dreams have been to me
In my young boyhood—should it thus be giv'n,
'T were folly still to hope for higher Heav'n.
For I have revell'd, when the sun was bright
I' the summer sky, in dreams of living light
And loveliness,—have left my very heart
In climes of mine imagining, apart
From mine own home, with beings that have been
Of mine own thought—what more could I have seen?
'T was once—and only once—and the wild hour
From my remembrance shall not pass—some pow'r
Or spell had bound me—'t was the chilly wind
Came o'er me in the night, and left behind
Its image on my spirit—or the moon
Shone on my slumbers in her lofty noon
Too coldly—or the stars—howe'er it was,
That dream was as that night-wind—let it pass.

I *have been* happy, tho' [but] in a dream.
I have been happy—and I love the theme:
Dreams! in their vivid coloring of life,
As in that fleeting, shadowy, misty strife
Of semblance with reality which brings
To the delirious eye, more lovely things
Of Paradise and Love—and all our own!
Than young Hope in his sunniest hour hath known.

Romance, who loves to nod and sing,
With drowsy head and folded wing,
Among the green leaves as they shake
Far down within some shadowy lake,
To me a painted paroquet
Hath been—a most familiar bird—
Taught me my alphabet to say,
To lisp my very earliest word,
While in the wild wood I did lie,
A child—with a most knowing eye.

Of late, eternal Condor years
So shake the very Heaven on high
With tumult as they thunder by,
I have no time for idle cares
Through gazing on the unquiet sky.
And when an hour with calmer wings
Its down upon my spirit flings—
That little time with lyre and rhyme
To while away—forbidden things!
My heart would feel to be a crime
Unless it trembled with the strings.

THE LAKE

In spring of youth it was my lot
To haunt of the wide world a spot
The which I could not love the less—
So lovely was the loneliness
Of a wild lake, with black rock bound,
And the tall pines that towered around.

But when the Night had thrown her pall
Upon that spot, as upon all,
And the mystic wind went by
Murmuring in melody,
Then—ah, then—I would awake
To the terror of the lone lake.

Yet that terror was not fright,
But a tremulous delight—
A feeling not the jewelled mine
Could teach or bribe me to define—
Nor Love—although the Love were thine.

Death was in that poisonous wave,
And in its gulf a fitting grave
For him who thence could solace bring
To his lone imagining,
Whose solitary soul could make
An Eden of that dim lake.

A DREAM WITHIN A DREAM

Take this kiss upon the brow!
And, in parting from you now,
Thus much let me avow:
You are not wrong, who deem
That my days have been a dream;
Yet if Hope has flown away
In a night, or in a day,
In a vision, or in none,
Is it therefore the less *gone*?
All that we see or seem
Is but a dream within a dream.

I stand amid the roar
Of a surf-tormented shore,
And I hold within my hand
Grains of the golden sand—
How few! yet how they creep
Through my fingers to the deep,
While I weep—while I weep!
O God! can I not grasp
Them with a tighter clasp?
O God! can I not save
One from the pitiless wave?
Is *all* that we see or seem
But a dream within a dream?

TO ONE IN PARADISE

Thou wast that all to me, love,
　For which my soul did pine—
A green isle in the sea, love,
　A fountain and a shrine,
All wreathed with fairy fruits and flowers,
　And all the flowers were mine.

Ah, dream too bright to last!
　Ah, starry Hope! that didst arise
But to be overcast!
　A voice from out the Future cries,
"On! on!"—but o'er the Past
　(Dim gulf!) my spirit hovering lies
Mute, motionless, aghast!

For, alas! alas! with me
　The light of Life is o'er!
No more—no more—no more—
　(Such language holds the solemn sea
To the sands upon the shore)
　Shall bloom the thunder-blasted tree,
Or the stricken eagle soar!

And all my days are trances,
　And all my nightly dreams
Are where thy grey eye glances,
　And where thy footstep gleams—
In what ethereal dances,
　By what eternal streams.

How often we forget all time, when lone
Admiring Nature's universal throne;
Her woods—her wilds—her mountains—the intense
Reply of HERS to our intelligence!
        BYRON: *The Island.*

In youth have I known one with whom the Earth
In secret communing held—as he with it,
In daylight, and in beauty from his birth:
Whose fervid, flickering torch of life was lit
From the sun and stars, whence he had drawn forth
A passionate light—such for his spirit was fit—
And yet that spirit knew not, in the hour
Of its own fervour, what had o'er it power.

Perhaps it may be that my mind is wrought
To a fever by the moonbeam that hangs o'er,
But I will half believe that wild light fraught
With more of sovereignty than ancient lore
Hath ever told;—or is it of a thought
The unembodied essence, and no more,
That with a quickening spell doth o'er us pass
As dew of the night-time o'er the summer grass?

Doth o'er us pass, when, as th' expanding eye
To the loved object,—so the tear to the lid
Will start, which lately slept in apathy?
And yet it need not be—(that object) hid
From us in life—but common—which doth lie
Each hour before us—but *then* only, bid
With a strange sound, as of a harp-string broken,
To awake us—'T is a symbol and a token
Of what in other worlds shall be—and given
In beauty by our God, to those alone
Who otherwise would fall from life and Heaven
Drawn by their heart's passion, and that tone,

That high tone of the spirit which hath striven,
Tho' not with Faith—with godliness—whose throne
With desperate energy 't hath beaten down;
Wearing its own deep feeling as a crown.

BRIDAL BALLAD

The ring is on my hand,
    And the wreath is on my brow;
Satins and jewels grand
Are all at my command,
    And I am happy now.

And my lord he loves me well;
    But, when first he breathed his vow,
I felt my bosom swell—
For the words rang as a knell,
And the voice seemed *his* who fell
In the battle down the dell,
    And who is happy now.

But he spoke to re-assure me,
    And he kissed my pallid brow,
While a reverie came o'er me,
And to the churchyard bore me,
And I sighed to him before me,
(Thinking him dead D'Elormie),
    "Oh, I am happy now!"

And thus the words were spoken;
  And this the plighted vow;
And, though my faith be broken,
And, though my heart be broken,
Here is a ring as token
  That I am happy now!
Behold the golden token
  That *proves* me happy now!

Would God I could awaken!
  For I dream I know not how,
And my soul is sorely shaken
Lest an evil step be taken,—
Lest the dead who is forsaken
  May not be happy now.

LENORE

Ah, broken is the golden bowl!—the spirit flown forever!
Let the bell toll!—a saintly soul floats on the Stygian river:—
And, Guy De Vere, hast *thou* no tear?—weep now or never
        more!
See! on yon drear and rigid bier low lies thy love, Lenore!
Come, let the burial rite be read—the funeral song be sung!—
An anthem for the queenliest dead that ever died so young—
A dirge for her the doubly dead in that she died so young.

"Wretches! ye loved her for her wealth, and ye hated her for
        her pride;
And, when she fell in feeble health, ye blessed her—that she
        died:—
How *shall* the ritual, then, be read—the requiem how be sung
By you—by yours, the evil eye,—by yours, the slanderous
        tongue
That did to death the innocence that died, and died so young?"

Peccavimus; yet rave not thus! but let a Sabbath song
Go up to God so solemnly the dead may feel no wrong!
The sweet Lenore hath gone before, with Hope that flew beside,
Leaving thee wild for the dear child that should have been thy
        bride—
For her, the fair and debonair, that now so lowly lies,
The life upon her yellow hair, but not within her eyes—
The life still there upon her hair, the death upon her eyes.

"Avaunt!—avaunt! to friends from fiends the indignant ghost is
        riven—
From Hell unto a high estate within the utmost Heaven—
From moan and groan to a golden throne beside the King of
        Heaven:—
Let *no* bell toll, then, lest her soul, amid its hallowed mirth,
Should catch the note as it doth float up from the damnéd Earth!
And I—to-night my heart is light:—no dirge will I upraise,
But waft the angel on her flight with a Paean of old days!"

AN ENIGMA

"Seldom we find," says Solomon Don Dunce,
  "Half an idea in the profoundest sonnet.
Through all the flimsy things we see at once
  As easily as through a Naples bonnet—
  Trash of all trash!—how *can* a lady don it?
Yet heavier far than your petrarchan stuff—
Owl-downy nonsense that the faintest puff
  Twirls into trunk-paper the while you con it."
And, veritably, Sol is right enough.
The general tuckermanities are arrant
Bubbles—ephemeral and *so* transparent—
But *this* is, now—you may depend upon it—
Stable, opaque, immortal—all by dint
Of the dear names that lie concealed within 't.

ELEONORA

Sub conservatione formae specificae salva anima.—RAYMOND LULLY

I AM come of a race noted for vigor of fancy and ardor of
passion. Men have called me mad; but the question is not yet
settled, whether madness is or is not the loftiest intelligence—
whether much that is glorious—whether all that is profound—
does not spring from disease of thought—from *moods* of mind
exalted at the expense of the general intellect. They who dream
by day are cognizant of many things which escape those who
dream only by night. In their grey visions they obtain glimpses
of eternity, and thrill, in awaking, to find that they have been

upon the verge of the great secret. In snatches, they learn something of the wisdom which is of good, and more of the mere knowledge which is of evil. They penetrate, however rudderless or compassless, into the vast ocean of the "light ineffable" and again, like the adventurers of the Nubian geographer, *"agressi sunt mare tenebrarum, quid in eo esset exploraturi."*

We will say, then, that I am mad. I grant, at least, that there are two distinct conditions of my mental existence—the condition of a lucid reason, not to be disputed, and belonging to the memory of events forming the first epoch of my life—and a condition of shadow and doubt, appertaining to the present, and to the recollection of what constitutes the second great era of my being. Therefore, what I shall tell of the earlier period, believe; and to what I may relate of the later time, give only such credit as may seem due; or doubt it altogether; or, if doubt it ye cannot, then play unto its riddle the Oedipus.

She whom I loved in youth, and of whom I now pen calmly and distinctly these remembrances, was the sole daughter of the only sister of my mother long departed. Eleonora was the name of my cousin. We had always dwelled together, beneath a tropical sun, in the Valley of the Many-Colored Grass. No unguided footstep ever came upon that vale; for it lay far away up among a range of giant hills that hung beetling around about it, shutting out the sunlight from its sweetest recesses. No path was trodden in its vicinity; and, to reach our happy home, there was need of putting back, with force, the foliage of many thousands of forest trees, and of crushing to death the glories of many millions of fragrant flowers. Thus it was that we lived all alone, knowing nothing of the world without the valley,—I, and my cousin, and her mother.

From the dim regions beyond the mountains at the upper end of our encircled domain, there crept out a narrow and deep river, brighter than all save the eyes of Eleonora; and, winding stealthily about in mazy courses, it passed away, at length, through a shadowy gorge, among hills still dimmer than those whence it had issued. We called it the "River of Silence"; for there seemed to be a hushing influence in its flow. No murmur arose from its bed, and so gently it wandered along, that the pearly pebbles upon which we loved to gaze, far down within its bosom, stirred not at all, but lay in a motionless content, each in its own old station, shining on gloriously forever.

The margin of the river, and of the many dazzling rivulets that glided, through devious ways, into its channel, as well as the spaces that extended from the margins away down into the depths of the streams until they reached the bed of pebbles at the bottom,—these spots, not less than the whole surface of the valley, from the river to the mountains that girdled it in, were carpeted all by a soft green grass, thick, short, perfectly even, and vanilla-perfumed, but so besprinkled throughout with the yellow buttercup, the white daisy, the purple violet, and the ruby-red asphodel, that its exceeding beauty spoke to our hearts, in loud tones, of the love and of the glory of God.

And, here and there, in groves about this grass, like wildernesses of dreams, sprang up fantastic trees, whose tall slender stems stood not upright, but slanted gracefully towards the light that peered at noon-day into the centre of the valley. Their bark was speckled with the vivid alternate splendor of ebony and silver, and was smoother than all save the cheeks of Eleonora; so that but for the brilliant green of the huge leaves that spread from their summits in long tremulous lines, dallying with the Zephyrs, one might have fancied them giant serpents of Syria doing homage to their Sovereign the Sun.

Hand in hand about this valley, for fifteen years, roamed I with Eleonora before Love entered within our hearts. It was one evening at the close of the third lustrum of her life, and of the fourth of my own, that we sat, locked in each other's embrace, beneath the serpent-like trees, and looked down within the waters of the River of Silence at our images therein. We spoke no words during the rest of that sweet day; and our words even upon the morrow were tremulous and few. We had drawn the god Eros from that wave, and now we felt that he had enkindled within us the fiery souls of our forefathers. The passions which had for centuries distinguished our race, came thronging with the fancies for which they had been equally noted, and together breathed a delirious bliss over the Valley of the Many-Colored Grass. A change fell upon all things. Strange brilliant flowers, star-shaped, burst out upon the trees where no flowers had been known before. The tints of the green carpet deepened; and when, one by one, the white daisies shrank away, there sprang up, in place of them, ten by ten of the ruby-red asphodel. And life arose in our paths; for the tall flamingo, hitherto unseen, with all gay glowing birds, flaunted his scarlet plumage before us. The golden and silver fish haunted the river, out of the bosom of which issued, little by little, a murmur that swelled, at length, into a lulling melody more divine than that of the harp of AEolus—sweeter than all save the voice of Eleonora. And now, too, a voluminous cloud, which we had long watched in the regions of Hesper, floated out thence, all gorgeous in crimson and gold, and settling in peace above us, sank, day by day, lower and lower, until its edges rested upon the tops of the mountains, turning all their dimness into magnificence, and shutting us up, as if forever, within a magic prison-house of grandeur and of glory.

The loveliness of Eleonora was that of the Seraphim; but she was a maiden artless and innocent as the brief life she had led among the flowers. No guile disguised the fervor of love which animated her heart, and she examined with me its inmost recesses as we walked together in the Valley of the Many-Colored Grass, and discoursed of the mighty changes which had lately taken place therein.

At length, having spoken one day, in tears, of the last sad change which must befall Humanity, she thenceforward dwelt only upon this one sorrowful theme, interweaving it into all our converse, as, in the songs of the bard of Schiraz, the same images are found occurring, again and again, in every impressive variation of phrase.

She had seen that the finger of Death was upon her bosom—that, like the ephemeron, she had been made perfect in loveliness only to die; but the terrors of the grave, to her, lay solely in a consideration which she revealed to me, one evening at twilight, by the banks of the River of Silence. She grieved to think that, having entombed her in the Valley of the Many-Colored Grass, I would quit forever its happy recesses, transferring the love which now was so passionately her own to some maiden of the outer and every-day world. And, then and there, I threw myself hurriedly at the feet of Eleonora, and offered up a vow, to herself and to Heaven, that I would never bind myself in marriage to any daughter of Earth—that I would in no manner prove recreant to her dear memory, or to the memory of the devout affection with which she had blessed me. And I called the Mighty Ruler of the Universe to witness the pious solemnity of my vow. And the curse which I invoked of *Him* and of her, a saint in Helusion, should I prove traitorous to that promise, involved a penalty the exceeding great horror of which will not permit me to make record of it here. And the bright eyes of Eleonora grew brighter at my words; and she sighed as if a deadly burthen had been taken from her breast; and she trembled and very bitterly wept; but she made acceptance of the vow, (for what was she but a child?) and it made easy to her the bed of her death. And she said to me, not many days afterwards, tranquilly dying, that, because of what I had done for the comfort of her spirit, she would watch over me in that spirit when departed, and, if so it were permitted her, return to me visibly in the watches of the night; but, if this thing were, indeed, beyond the power of the souls in Paradise, that she would, at least, give me frequent indications of her presence; sighing upon me in the evening winds, or filling the air which I breathed with perfume from the censers of the angels. And, with these words upon her lips, she yielded up her innocent life, putting an end to the first epoch of my own.

Thus far I have faithfully said. But as I pass the barrier in Time's path formed by the death of my beloved, and proceed with the second era of my existence, I feel that a shadow gathers over my brain, and I mistrust the perfect sanity of the record. But let me on.—Years dragged themselves along heavily, and still I dwelled within the Valley of the Many-Colored Grass;—but a second change had come upon all things. The star-shaped flowers shrank into the stems of the trees, and appeared no more. The tints of the green carpet faded; and, one by one, the ruby-red asphodels withered away; and there sprang up, in place of them, ten by ten, dark eye-like violets that writhed uneasily and were ever encumbered with dew. And Life departed from our paths; for the tall flamingo flaunted no longer his scarlet plumage before us, but flew sadly from the vale into the hills, with all the gay glowing birds that had arrived in his company. And the golden and silver fish swam down through the gorge at the lower end of our domain and bedecked the sweet river never again. And the lulling melody that had been softer than the wind-harp of AEolus and more divine than all save the voice of Eleonora, it died little by little away, in murmurs growing lower and lower, until the stream returned, at length, utterly, into the solemnity of its original silence. And then, lastly the voluminous cloud uprose, and, abandoning the tops of the mountains to the dimness of old, fell back into the regions of Hesper, and took away all its manifold golden and gorgeous glories from the Valley of the Many-Colored Grass.

Yet the promises of Eleonora were not forgotten; for I heard the sounds of the swinging of the censers of the angels; the streams of a holy perfume floated ever and ever about the valley; and at lone hours, when my heart beat heavily, the winds that bathed my brow came unto me laden with soft sighs; and indistinct murmurs filled often the night air; and once—oh, but once only! I was awakened from a slumber like the slumber of death by the pressing of spiritual lips upon my own.

But the void within my heart refused, even thus, to be filled. I longed for the love which had before filled it to overflowing. At length the valley *pained* me through its memories of Eleonora, and I left it forever for the vanities and the turbulent triumphs of the world.

I found myself within a strange city, where all things might have served to blot from recollection the sweet dreams I had dreamed so long in the Valley of the Many-Colored Grass. The pomps and pageantries of a stately court, and the mad clangor of arms, and the radiant loveliness of woman, bewildered and intoxicated my brain. But as yet my soul had proved true to its vows, and the indications of the presence of Eleonora were still given me in the silent hours of the night. Suddenly, these manifestations they ceased; and the world grew dark before mine eyes; and I stood aghast at the burning thoughts which possessed—at the terrible temptations which beset me; for there came from some far, far distant and unknown land, into the gay court of the king I served, a maiden to whose beauty my whole recreant heart yielded at once—at whose footstool I bowed down without a struggle, in the most ardent, in the most abject worship of love. What indeed was my passion for the young girl of the valley in comparison with the fervor, and the delirium, and the spirit-lifting ecstasy of adoration with which I poured out my whole soul in tears at the feet of the ethereal Ermengarde?—Oh bright was the seraph Ermengarde! and in that knowledge I had room for none other. Oh divine was the angel Ermengarde! and as I looked down into the depths of her memorial eyes I thought only of them—and *of her*.

I wedded;—nor dreaded the curse I had invoked; and its bitterness was not visited upon me. And once—but once again in the silence of the night, there came through my lattice the soft sighs which had forsaken me; and they modelled themselves into familiar and sweet voice, saying:

"Sleep in peace!—for the Spirit of Love reigneth and ruleth, and, in taking to thy passionate heart her who is Ermengarde, thou art absolved, for reasons which shall be made known to thee in Heaven, of thy vows unto Eleonora."

TO HELEN

I saw thee once—once only—years ago:
I must not say *how* many—but *not* many.
It was a July midnight; and from out
A full-orbed moon, that, like thine own soul, soaring,
Sought a precipitate pathway up through heaven,
There fell a silvery-silken veil of light,
With quietude, and sultriness, and slumber,
Upon the upturn'd faces of a thousand
Roses that grew in an enchanted garden,
Where no wind dared to stir, unless on tiptoe—
Fell on the upturn'd faces of these roses
That gave out, in return for the love-light,
Their odorous souls in an ecstatic death—
Fell on the upturn'd faces of these roses
That smiled and died in this parterre, enchanted
By thee, and by the poetry of thy presence.

Clad all in white, upon a violet bank
I saw thee half reclining; while the moon
Fell on the upturn'd faces of the roses,
And on thine own, upturn'd—alas, in sorrow!

Was it not Fate that, on this July midnight—
Was it not Fate (whose name is also Sorrow)
That bade me pause before that garden-gate,
To breathe the incense of those slumbering roses?
No footstep stirred: the hated world all slept,
Save only thee and me. (Oh, Heaven!—oh, God!
How my heart beats in coupling those two words!)
Save only thee and me.) I paused—I looked—
And in an instant all things disappeared.
(Ah, bear in mind this garden was enchanted!)
The pearly lustre of the moon went out:
The mossy banks and the meandering paths,
The happy flowers and the repining trees,

Were seen no more: the very roses' odors
Died in the arms of the adoring airs.
All—all expired save thee—save less than thou:
Save only the divine light in thine eyes—
Save but the soul in thine uplifted eyes.
I saw but them—they were the world to me.
I saw but them—saw only them for hours—
Saw only them until the moon went down.
What wild heart-histories seemed to lie enwritten
Upon those crystalline, celestial spheres!
How dark a wo! yet how sublime a hope!
How silently serene a sea of pride!
How daring an ambition! yet how deep—
How fathomless a capacity for love!

But now, at length, dear Dian sank from sight,
Into a western couch of thunder-cloud;
And thou, a ghost, amid the entombing trees
Didst glide away. *Only thine eyes remained.*
They *would not* go—they never yet have gone.
Lighting my lonely pathway home that night,
They have not left me (as my hopes have) since.
They follow me—they lead me through the years.
They are my ministers—yet I their slave.
Their office is to illumine and enkindle—
My duty, *to be saved* by their bright light,
And purified in their electric fire,
And sanctified in their elysian fire.
They fill my soul with Beauty (which is Hope),
And are far up in Heaven—the stars I kneel to
In the sad, silent watches of my night;
While even in the meridian glare of day
I see them still—two sweetly scintillant
Venuses, unextinguished by the sun!

EULALIE—A SONG

I dwelt alone
In a world of moan,
And my soul was a stagnant tide,
Till the fair and gentle Eulalie became my blushing bride—
Till the yellow-haired young Eulalie became my smiling bride.

Ah, less—less bright
The stars of the night
Than the eyes of the radiant girl!
And never a flake
That the vapor can make
With the moon-tints of purple and pearl,
Can vie with the modest Eulalie's most unregarded curl—
Can compare with the bright-eyed Eulalie's most humble and
careless curl.

Now Doubt—now Pain
Come never again,
For her soul gives me sigh for sigh,
And all day long
Shines, bright and strong,
Astarté within the sky,
While ever to her dear Eulalie upturns her matron eye—
While ever to her young Eulalie upturns her violet eye.

ANNABEL LEE

It was many and many a year ago,
    In a kingdom by the sea,
That a maiden there lived whom you may know
    By the name of Annabel Lee;—
And this maiden she lived with no other thought
    Than to love and be loved by me.

She was a child and *I* was a child,
    In this kingdom by the sea,
But we loved with a love that was more than love—
    I and my Annabel Lee—
With a love that the wingéd seraphs of Heaven
    Coveted her and me.

And this was the reason that, long ago,
    In this kingdom by the sea,
A wind blew out of a cloud by night
    Chilling my Annabel Lee;
So that her highborn kinsmen came
    And bore her away from me,
To shut her up in a sepulchre
    In this kingdom by the sea.

The angels, not half so happy in Heaven,
    Went envying her and me:—
Yes! that was the reason (as all men know,
    In this kingdom by the sea)
That the wind came out of the cloud, chilling
    And killing my Annabel Lee.

But our love it was stronger by far than the love
    Of those who were older than we—
    Of many far wiser than we—
And neither the angels in Heaven above
    Nor the demons down under the sea,

Can ever dissever my soul from the soul
  Of the beautiful Annabel Lee:—

For the moon never beams without bringing me dreams
  Of the beautiful Annabel Lee;
And the stars never rise but I see the bright eyes
  Of the beautiful Annabel Lee;
And so, all the night-tide, I lie down by the side
Of my darling, my darling, my life and my bride,
  In her sepulchre there by the sea—
  In her tomb by the side of the sea.

TO MY MOTHER

Because I feel that, in the Heavens above,
  The angels, whispering to one another,
Can find, among their burning terms of love,
  None so devotional as that of "Mother,"
Therefore by that dear name I long have called you—
  You who are more than mother unto me,
And fill my heart of hearts, where Death installed you
  In setting my Virginia's spirit free.
My mother—my own mother, who died early,
  Was but the mother of myself; but you
Are mother to the one I loved so dearly,
  And thus are dearer than the mother I knew
By that infinity with which my wife
  Was dearer to my soul than its soul-life.

IV. CRITICISM

LETTER TO B———

Dear B———.

*   *   *

It has been said, that a good critique on a poem may be written by one who is no poet himself. This, according to *your* idea and *mine* of poetry, I feel to be false—the less poetical the critic, the less just the critique, and the converse. On this account, and because there are but few B———s in the world, I would be as much ashamed of the world's good opinion as proud of your own. Another than yourself might here observe "Shakspeare is in possession of the world's good opinion, and yet Shakspeare is the greatest of poets. It appears then that the world judge correctly, why should you be ashamed of their favorable judgment?" The difficulty lies in the interpretation of the word "judgment" or "opinion." The opinion is the world's, truly, but it may be called theirs as a man would call a book his, having bought it; he did not write the book, but it is his; they did not originate the opinion, but it is theirs. A fool, for example, thinks Shakspeare a great poet—yet the fool has never read Shakspeare. But the fool's neighbor, who is a step higher on the Andes of the mind, whose head (that is to say his more exalted thought) is too far above the fool to be seen or understood, but whose feet (by which I mean his every day actions) are sufficiently near to be discerned, and by means of which that superiority is ascertained, which *but* for them would never have been discovered—this neighbor asserts that Shakspeare is a great poet—the fool believes him, and it is henceforward his *opinion*. This neighbor's own opinion has, in like manner, been adopted from one above *him*, and so, ascendingly, to a few gifted individuals, who kneel around the summit, beholding, face to face, the master spirit who stands upon the pinnacle.

I mentioned just now a vulgar error as regards criticism. I think the notion that no poet can form a correct estimate of his own writings is another. I remarked before, that in proportion to the poetical talent, would be the justice of a critique upon poetry. Therefore, a bad poet would, I grant, make a false critique, and his self-love would infallibly bias his little judgment in his favor; but a poet, who is indeed a poet, could not, I think, fail of making a just critique. Whatever should be deducted on the score of self-love, might be replaced on account of his intimate acquaintance with the subject; in short, we have more instances of false criticism than of just, where one's own writings are the test, simply because we have more bad poets than good. There are of course many objections to what I say: Milton is a great example of the contrary; but his opinion with respect to the Paradise Regained, is by no means fairly ascertained. By what trivial circumstances men are often led to assert what they do not really believe! Perhaps an inadvertent word has descended to posterity. But, in fact, the Paradise Regained is little, if at all, inferior to the Paradise Lost, and is only supposed so to be because men do not like epics, whatever they may say to the contrary, and reading those of Milton in their natural order, are too much wearied with the first to derive any pleasure from the second.

I dare say Milton preferred Comus to either—if so—justly.

As I am speaking of poetry, it will not be amiss to touch slightly upon the most singular heresy in its modern history— the heresy of what is called very foolishly, the Lake School. Some years ago I might have been induced, by an occasion like the present, to attempt a formal refutation of their doctrine; at present it would be a work of supererogation. The wise must bow to the wisdom of such men as Coleridge and Southey, but being wise, have laughed at poetical theories so prosaically exemplified.

Aristotle, with singular assurance, has declared poetry the most philosophical of all writing—but it required a Wordsworth to pronounce it the most metaphysical. He seems to think that the end of poetry is, or should be, instruction—yet it is a truism that the end of our existence is happiness; if so, the end of every separate part of our existence—every thing connected with our existence should be still happiness. Therefore the end of instruction should be happiness; and happiness is another name for pleasure;—therefore the end of instruction should be pleasure: yet we see the above mentioned opinion implies precisely the reverse.

To proceed: *ceteris paribus,* he who pleases, is of more importance to his fellow men than he who instructs, since utility is happiness, and pleasure is the end already obtained which instruction is merely the means of obtaining.

I see no reason, then, why our metaphysical poets should plume themselves so much on the utility of their works, unless indeed they refer to instruction with eternity in view; in which case, sincere respect for their piety would not allow me to express my contempt for their judgment; contempt which it would be difficult to conceal, since their writings are professedly to be understood by the few, and it is the many who stand in need of salvation. In such case I should no doubt be tempted to think of the devil in Melmoth, who labors indefatigably through three octavo volumes, to accomplish the destruction of one or two souls, while any common devil would have demolished one or two thousand.

Against the subtleties which would make poetry a study—not a passion—it becomes the metaphysician to reason—but the poet to protest. Yet Wordsworth and Coleridge are men in years; the one imbued in contemplation from his childhood, the other a giant in intellect and learning. The diffidence, then, with which I venture to dispute their authority would be overwhelming, did I not feel, from the bottom of my heart, that learning has little to do with the imagination—intellect with the passions—or age with poetry. . . .

"Trifles, like straws, upon the surface flow,
  He who would search for pearls must dive below,"

111

are lines which have done much mischief. As regards the greater truths, men oftener err by seeking them at the bottom than at the top; the depth lies in the huge abysses where wisdom is sought—not in the palpable palaces where she is found. The ancients were not always right in hiding the goddess in a well: witness the light which Bacon has thrown upon philosophy; witness the principles of our divine faith—that moral mechanism by which the simplicity of a child may overbalance the wisdom of a man.

Poetry, above all things, is a beautiful painting whose tints, to minute inspection, are confusion worse confounded, but start boldly out to the cursory glance of the connoisseur.

We see an instance of Coleridge's liability to err in his Biographia Literaria—professedly his literary life and opinions, but, in fact, a treatise *de omni scibili et quibusdam aliis*. He goes wrong by reason of his very profundity, and of his error we have a natural type in the contemplation of a star. He who regards it directly and intensely sees, it is true, the star, but it is the star without a ray—while he who surveys it less inquisitively is conscious of all for which the star is useful to us below —its brilliancy and its beauty.

As to Wordsworth, I have no faith in him: That he had, in youth, the feelings of a poet, I believe—for there are glimpses of extreme delicacy in his writings—(and delicacy is the poet's own kingdom—his *El Dorado*)—but they have the appearance of a better day recollected; and glimpses, at best, are little evidence of present poetic fire—we know that a few straggling flowers spring up daily in the crevices of the Avalanche.

He was to blame in wearing away his youth in contemplation with the end of poetizing in his manhood. With the increase of his judgment the light which should make it apparent has faded away. His judgment consequently is too correct. This may not be understood, but the old Goths of Germany would have understood it, who used to debate matters of importance to their State twice, once when drunk, and once when sober—

sober that they might not be deficient in formality—drunk lest they should be destitute of vigor.

The long wordy discussions by which he tries to reason us into admiration of his poetry, speak very little in his favor: they are full of such assertions as this—(I have opened one of his volumes at random) "Of genius the only proof is the act of doing well what is worthy to be done, and what was never done before"—indeed! then it follows that in doing what is *un*worthy to be done, or what *has* been done before, no genius can be evinced: yet the picking of pockets is an unworthy act, pockets have been picked time immemorial, and Barrington, the pick-pocket, in point of genius, would have thought hard of a comparison with William Wordsworth, the poet.

Again—in estimating the merit of certain poems, whether they be Ossian's or M'Pherson's, can surely be of little consequence, yet, in order to prove their worthlessness, Mr. W. has expended many pages in the controversy. *Tantoene animis?* Can great minds descend to such absurdity? But worse still: that he may bear down every argument in favor of these poems, he triumphantly drags forward a passage in his abomination of which he expects the reader to sympathize. It is the beginning of the epic poem *"Temora."* "The blue waves of Ullin roll in light; the green hills are covered with day; trees shake their dusky heads in the breeze." And this—this gorgeous, yet simple imagery—where all is alive and panting with immortality— than which earth has nothing more grand, nor paradise more beautiful—this—William Wordsworth, the author of Peter Bell, has *selected* to dignify with his imperial contempt. We shall see what better he, in his own person, has to offer. Imprimis:

"And now she's at the poney's head,
And now she's at the poney's tail,
On that side now, and now on this,
And almost stifled her with bliss—
A few sad tears does Betty shed,
She pats the poney where or when
She knows not: happy Betty Foy!
O Johnny! never mind the Doctor!"

Secondly:

> "The dew was falling fast, the—stars began to blink,
> I heard a voice, it said—drink, pretty creature, drink;
> And looking o'er the hedge, be—fore me I espied
> A snow-white mountain lamb with a—maiden at its side.
> No other sheep were near, the lamb was all alone,
> And by a slender cord was—tether'd to a stone."

Now we have no doubt this is all true; we *will* believe it, indeed we will, Mr. W. Is it sympathy for the sheep you wish to excite? I love a sheep from the bottom of my heart.

Of Coleridge I cannot speak but with reverence. His towering intellect! his gigantic power! To use an author quoted by himself, "J'ai trouvé souvent que la plupart des sectes ont raison dans une bonne partie de ce quelles avancent, mais non pas en ce quelles nient," and, to employ his own language, he has imprisoned his own conceptions by the barrier he has erected against those of others. It is lamentable to think that such a mind should be buried in metaphysics, and, like the Nyctanthes, waste its perfume upon the night alone. In reading that man's poetry I tremble, like one who stands upon a volcano, conscious, from the very darkness bursting from the crater, of the fire and the light that are weltering below.

What is Poetry? Poetry! that Proteus-like idea, with as many appellations as the nine-titled Corcyra! Give me, I demanded of a scholar some time ago, give me a definition of poetry? "Tres volontiers,"—and he proceeded to his library, brought me a Dr. Johnson, and overwhelmed me with a definition. Shade of the immortal Shakspeare! I imagined to myself the scowl of your spiritual eye upon the profanity of that scurrilous Ursa Major. Think of poetry, dear B———, think of poetry, and then think of—Dr. Samuel Johnson! Think of all that is airy and fairy-like, and then of all that is hideous and unwieldy; think of his huge bulk, the Elephant! and then—and then think of the Tempest—the Midsummer Night's Dream—Prospero—Oberon—and Titania!

A poem, in my opinion, is opposed to a work of science by having, for its *immediate* object, pleasure, not truth; to romance, by having for its object an *indefinite* instead of a *definite* pleasure, being a poem only so far as this object is attained: romance presenting perceptible images with definite, poetry with *in*definite sensations, to which end music is an *essential*, since the comprehension of sweet sound is our most indefinite conception. Music, when combined with a pleasurable idea, is poetry; music without the idea is simply music; the idea without the music is prose from its very definitiveness.

What was meant by the invective against "him who had no music in his soul?"

To sum up this long rigmarole, I have, dear B———, what you no doubt perceive, for the metaphysical poets, *as* poets, the most sovereign contempt. That they have followers proves nothing—

> No Indian prince has to his palace
> More followers than a thief to the gallows.

THE PHILOSOPHY OF COMPOSITION

CHARLES DICKENS, in a note now lying before me, alluding to an examination I once made of the mechanism of "Barnaby Rudge," says—"By the way, are you aware that Godwin wrote his 'Caleb Williams' backwards? He first involved his hero in a web of difficulties, forming the second volume, and then, for the first, cast about him for some mode of accounting for what had been done."

I cannot think this the *precise* mode of procedure on the part of Godwin—and indeed what he himself acknowledges, is not altogether in accordance with Mr. Dickens' idea—but the author of "Caleb Williams" was too good an artist not to perceive the advantage derivable from at least a somewhat similar process. Nothing is more clear than that every plot, worth the name, must be elaborated to its *dénouement* before anything be attempted with the pen. It is only with the *dénouement* constantly in view that we can give a plot its indispensable air of consequence, or causation, by making the incidents, and especially the tone at all points, tend to the development of the intention.

There is a radical error, I think, in the usual mode of constructing a story. Either history affords a thesis—or one is suggested by an incident of the day—or, at best, the author sets himself to work in the combination of striking events to form merely the basis of his narrative—designing, generally, to fill in with description, dialogue, or authorial comment, whatever crevices of fact, or action, may, from page to page, render themselves apparent.

I prefer commencing with the consideration of an *effect.* Keeping originality *always* in view—for he is false to himself who ventures to dispense with so obvious and so easily attainable a source of interest—I say to myself, in the first place, "Of the innumerable effects, or impressions, of which the heart, the intellect, or (more generally) the soul is susceptible, what one shall I, on the present occasion, select?" Having chosen a novel, first, and secondly a vivid effect, I consider whether it can be best wrought by incident or tone—whether by ordinary incidents and peculiar tone, or the converse, or by peculiarity both of incident and tone—afterward looking about me (or rather within) for such combinations of event, or tone, as shall best aid me in the construction of the effect.

I have often thought how interesting a magazine paper might be written by any author who would—that is to say who could —detail, step by step, the processes by which any one of his compositions attained its ultimate point of completion. Why such a paper has never been given to the world, I am much at a loss to say—but, perhaps, the authorial vanity has had more to do with the omission than any one other cause. Most writers— poets in especial—prefer having it understood that they compose by a species of fine frenzy—an ecstatic intuition—and would positively shudder at letting the public take a peep behind the scenes, at the elaborate and vacillating crudities of thought— at the true purposes seized only at the last moment—at the innumerable glimpses of idea that arrived not at the maturity of full view—at the fully matured fancies discarded in despair as unmanageable—at the cautious selections and rejections—at the painful erasures and interpolations—in a word, at the wheels and pinions—the tackle for scene-shifting—the step-ladders and demon-traps—the cock's feather's, the red paint and the black patches, which, in ninety-nine cases out of the hundred, constitute the properties of the literary *histrio*.

I am aware, on the other hand, that the case is by no means common, in which an author is at all in condition to retrace the steps by which his conclusions have been attained. In general, suggestions, having arisen pell-mell, are pursued and forgotten in a similar manner.

For my own part, I have neither sympathy with the repugnance alluded to, nor, at any time the least difficulty in recalling to mind the progressive steps of any of my compositions; and since the interest of an analysis, or reconstruction, such as I have considered a *desideratum,* is quite independent of any real or fancied interest in the thing analyzed, it will not be regarded as a breach of decorum on my part to show the *modus operandi* by which some one of my own works was put together. I select

"The Raven," as most generally known. It is my design to render it manifest that no one point in its composition is referrible either to accident or intuition—that the work proceeded, step by step, to its completion with the precision and rigid consequence of a mathematical problem.

Let us dismiss, as irrelevant to the poem, *per se*, the circumstance—or say the necessity—which, in the first place, gave rise to the intention of composing *a* poem that should suit at once the popular and the critical taste.

We commence, then, with this intention.

The initial consideration was that of extent. If any literary work is too long to be read at one sitting, we must be content to dispense with the immensely important effect derivable from unity of impression—for, if two sittings be required, the affairs of the world interfere, and every thing like totality is at once destroyed. But since, *ceteris paribus*, no poet can afford to dispense with *any thing* that may advance his design, it but remains to be seen whether there is, in extent, any advantage to counterbalance the loss of unity which attends it. Here I say no, at once. What we term a long poem is, in fact, merely a succession of brief ones —that is to say, of brief poetical effects. It is needless to demonstrate that a poem is such, only inasmuch as it intensely excites, by elevating, the soul; and all intense excitements are, through a psychal necessity, brief. For this reason, at least one half of the "Paradise Lost" is essentially prose—a succession of poetical excitements interspersed, *inevitably*, with corresponding depressions—the whole being deprived, through the extremeness of its length, of the vastly important artistic element, totality, or unity, of effect.

It appears evident, then, that there is a distinct limit, as regards length, to all works of literary art—the limit of a single sitting—and that, although in certain classes of prose composition, such as "Robinson Crusoe," (demanding no unity,) this limit may be advantageously overpassed, it can never properly be overpassed in a poem. Within this limit, the extent of a poem may be made to bear mathematical relation to its merit—in other words, to the excitement or elevation—again in other words, to the degree of the true poetical effect which it is capable of inducing; for it is clear that the brevity must be in direct ratio of the intensity of the intended effect:—this, with one proviso—that a certain degree of duration is absolutely requisite for the production of any effect at all.

Holding in view these considerations, as well as that degree of excitement which I deemed not above the popular, while not below the critical, taste, I reached at once what I conceived the proper *length* for my intended poem—a length of about one hundred lines. It is, in fact, a hundred and eight.

My next thought concerned the choice of an impression, or effect, to be conveyed: and here I may as well observe that, throughout the construction, I kept steadily in view the design of rendering the work *universally* appreciable. I should be carried too far out of my immediate topic were I to demonstrate a point upon which I have repeatedly insisted, and which, with the poetical, stands not in the slightest need of demonstration—the point, I mean, that Beauty is the sole legitimate province of the poem. A few words, however, in elucidation of my real meaning, which some of my friends have evinced a disposition to misrepresent. That pleasure which is at once the most intense, the most elevating, and the most pure, is, I believe, found in the contemplation of the beautiful. When, indeed, men speak of Beauty, they mean, precisely, not a quality, as is supposed, but an effect—they refer, in short, just to that intense and pure elevation of *soul*—*not* of intellect, or of heart—upon which I have commented, and which is experienced in consequence of contemplating "the beautiful." Now I designate Beauty as the province of the poem, merely because it is an obvious rule of Art that effects should be made to spring from direct causes—that objects should be attained through means best adapted for their attainment—no one as yet having been weak enough to deny that the peculiar elevation alluded to is *most readily* attained in the poem. Now the object Truth, or the satisfaction of the intellect, and the object Passion, or the excitement of the heart, are, although attainable, to a certain extent, in poetry, far more readily attainable in prose. Truth, in fact, demands a precision, and Passion a *homeliness* (the truly passionate will comprehend me) which are absolutely antagonistic to that Beauty which, I maintain, is the excitement, or pleasurable elevation, of the soul. It by no means follows from any thing here said, that passion, or even truth, may not be introduced, and even profitably introduced, into a poem—for they may serve in elucidation, or aid the general effect, as do discords in music, by contrast—but the true artist will always contrive, first, to tone them into proper subservience to the predominant aim, and, secondly, to enveil them, as far as possible, in that Beauty which is the atmosphere and the essence of the poem.

Regarding, then, Beauty as my province, my next question referred to the *tone* of its highest manifestation—and all experience has shown that this tone is one of *sadness*. Beauty of whatever kind, in its supreme development, invariably excites the sensitive soul to tears. Melancholy is thus the most legitimate of all the poetical tones.

The length, the province, and the tone, being thus determined, I betook myself to ordinary induction, with the view of obtaining some artistic piquancy which might serve me as a key-note in the construction of the poem—some pivot upon which the whole structure might turn. In carefully thinking over all the usual artistic effects—or more properly *points*, in the theatrical sense—I did not fail to perceive immediately that no one had been so universally employed as that of the *refrain*. The universality of its employment sufficed to assure me of its intrinsic value, and spared me the necessity of submitting it to analysis. I considered it, however, with regard to its susceptibility of improvement, and soon saw it to be in a primitive condition. As commonly used, the *refrain*, or burden, not only is limited to lyric verse, but depends for its impression upon the force of monotone—both in sound and thought. The pleasure is deduced solely from the sense of identity—of repetition. I resolved to diversify, and so heighten, the effect, by adhering, in general, to the monotone of sound, while I continually varied that of thought: that is to say, I determined to produce continuously novel effects, by the variation *of the application* of the *refrain*—the *refrain* itself remaining, for the most part, unvaried.

These points being settled, I next bethought me of the *nature* of my *refrain*. Since its application was to be repeatedly varied, it was clear that the *refrain* itself must be brief, for there would have been an insurmountable difficulty in frequent variations of application in any sentence of length. In proportion to the brevity of the sentence, would, of course, be the facility of the variation. This led me at once to a single word as the best *refrain*.

The question now arose as to the *character* of the word. Having made up my mind to a *refrain*, the division of the poem into stanzas was, of course, a corollary: the *refrain* forming the close of each stanza. That such a close, to have force, must be sonorous and susceptible of protracted emphasis, admitted no doubt: and these considerations inevitably led me to the long *o* as the most sonorous vowel, in connection with *r* as the most producible consonant.

The sound of the *refrain* being thus determined, it became necessary to select a word embodying this sound, and at the same time in the fullest possible keeping with that melancholy which I had predetermined as the tone of the poem. In such a search it would have been absolutely impossible to overlook the word "Nevermore." In fact, it was the very first which presented itself.

The next *desideratum* was a pretext for the continuous use of the one word "nevermore." In observing the difficulty which I at once found in inventing a sufficiently plausible reason for its continuous repetition, I did not fail to perceive that this difficulty arose solely from the pre-assumption that the word was to be so continuously or monotonously spoken by a *human* being—I did not fail to perceive, in short, that the difficulty lay in the reconciliation of this monotony with the exercise of reason on the part of the creature repeating the word. Here, then, immediately arose the idea of a *non*-reasoning creature capable of speech; and, very naturally, a parrot, in the first instance, suggested itself, but was superseded forthwith by a Raven, as equally capable of speech, and infinitely more in keeping with the intended *tone*.

I had now gone so far as the conception of a Raven—the bird of ill omen—monotonously repeating the one word, "Nevermore," at the conclusion of each stanza, in a poem of melancholy tone, and in length about one hundred lines. Now, never losing sight of the object *supremeness*, or perfection, at all points, I asked myself—"Of all melancholy topics, what, according to the *universal* understanding of mankind, is the *most* melancholy?" Death—was the obvious reply. "And when," I said, "is this most melancholy of topics most poetical?" From what I have already explained at some length, the answer, here also, is obvious—"When it most closely allies itself to *Beauty:* the death, then, of a beautiful woman is, unquestionably, the most poetical topic in the world—and equally is it beyond doubt that the lips best suited for such topic are those of a bereaved lover."

I had now to combine the two ideas, of a lover lamenting his deceased mistress and a Raven continuously repeating the word "Nevermore."—I had to combine these, bearing in mind my design of varying, at every turn, the *application* of the word repeated; but the only intelligible mode of such combination is that of imagining the Raven employing the word in answer to the queries of the lover. And here it was that I saw at once the opportunity afforded for the effect on which I had been depending—that is to say, the effect of the *variation of application*. I saw that I could make the first query propounded by the lover—the first query to which the Raven should reply "Nevermore"—that I could make this first query a commonplace one—the second less so—the third still less, and so on—until at length the lover, startled from his original *nonchalance* by the melancholy character of the word itself—by its frequent repetition—and by a consideration of the ominous reputation of the fowl that uttered it—is at length excited to superstition, and wildly propounds queries of a far different character—queries whose solution he has passionately at heart—propounds them half in superstition and half in that species of despair which delights in self-torture—propounds them not altogether because he believes in the prophetic or demoniac character of the bird (which, reason assures him, is merely repeating a lesson learned by rote) but because he experiences a phrenzied pleasure in so modeling his questions as to receive from the *expected* "Nevermore" the most delicious because the most intolerable of sorrow. Perceiving the opportunity thus afforded me—or, more strictly, thus forced upon me in the progress of the construction—I first established in mind the climax, or concluding query—that query to which "Nevermore" should be in the last place an answer—that in reply to which this word "Nevermore" should involve the utmost conceivable amount of sorrow and despair.

Here then the poem may be said to have its beginning—at the end, where all works of art should begin—for it was here, at this point of my preconsiderations, that I first put pen to paper in the composition of the stanza:

> "Prophet," said I, "thing of evil! prophet still if bird or devil!
> By that heaven that bends above us—by that God we both adore,
> Tell this soul with sorrow laden, if within the distant Aidenn,
> It shall clasp a sainted maiden whom the angels name Lenore—
> Clasp a rare and radiant maiden whom the angels name Lenore."
> Quoth the raven "Nevermore."

I composed this stanza, at this point, first that, by establishing the climax, I might the better vary and graduate, as regards seriousness and importance, the preceding queries of the lover —and, secondly, that I might definitely settle the rhythm, the metre, and the length and general arrangement of the stanza—as well as graduate the stanzas which were to precede, so that none of them might surpass this in rhythmical effect. Had I been able, in the subsequent composition, to construct more vigorous stanzas, I should, without scruple, have purposely enfeebled them, so as not to interfere with the climacteric effect.

And here I may as well say a few words of the versification. My first object (as usual) was originality. The extent to which this has been neglected, in versification, is one of the most unaccountable things in the world. Admitting that there is little possibility of variety in mere *rhythm*, it is still clear that the possible varieties of metre and stanza are absolutely infinite—and yet, *for centuries, no man, in verse, has ever done, or ever seemed to think of doing, an original thing.* The fact is, that originality (unless in minds of very unusual force) is by no means a matter, as some suppose, of impulse or intuition. In general, to be found, it must be elaborately sought, and although a positive merit of the highest class, demands in its attainment less of invention than negation.

Of course, I pretend to no originality in either the rhythm or metre of the "Raven." The former is trochaic—the latter is octameter acatalectic, alternating with heptameter catalectic repeated in the *refrain* of the fifth verse, and terminating with tetrameter catalectic. Less pedantically—the feet employed throughout (trochees) consist of a long syllable followed by a short: the first line of the stanza consists of eight of these feet—the second of seven and a half (in effect two-thirds)—the third of eight—the fourth of seven and a half—the fifth the same—the sixth three and a half. Now, each of these lines, taken individually, has been employed before, and what originality the "Raven" has, is in their *combination into stanza;* nothing even remotely approaching this combination has ever been attempted. The effect of this originality of combination is aided by other unusual, and some altogether novel effects, arising from an extension of the application of the principles of rhyme and alliteration.

The next point to be considered was the mode of bringing together the lover and the Raven—and the first branch of this consideration was the *locale.* For this the most natural suggestion might seem to be a forest, or the fields—but it has always appeared to me that a close *circumscription of space* is absolutely necessary to the effect of insulated incident:—it has the force of a frame to a picture. It has an indisputable moral power in keeping concentrated the attention, and, of course, must not be confounded with mere unity of place.

I determined, then, to place the lover in his chamber—in a chamber rendered sacred to him by memories of her who had frequented it. The room is represented as richly furnished —this in mere pursuance of the ideas I have already explained on the subject of Beauty, as the sole true poetical thesis.

The *locale* being thus determined, I had now to introduce the bird—and the thought of introducing him through the window, was inevitable. The idea of making the lover suppose, in the first instance, that the flapping of the wings of the bird against the shutter, is a "tapping" at the door, originated in a wish to increase, by prolonging, the reader's curiosity, and in a desire to admit the incidental effect arising from the lover's throwing open the door, finding all dark, and thence adopting the half-fancy that it was the spirit of his mistress that knocked.

I made the night tempestuous, first, to account for the Raven's seeking admission, and secondly, for the effect of contrast with the (physical) serenity within the chamber.

I made the bird alight on the bust of Pallas, also for the effect of contrast between the marble and the plumage—it being understood that the bust was absolutely *suggested* by the bird—the bust of *Pallas* being chosen, first, as most in keeping with the scholarship of the lover, and, secondly, for the sonorousness of the word, Pallas, itself.

About the middle of the poem, also, I have availed myself of the force of contrast, with a view of deepening the ultimate impression. For example, an air of the fantastic—approaching as nearly to the ludicrous as was admissible—is given to the Raven's entrance. He comes in "with many a flirt and flutter."

Not the *least obeisance made he*—not a moment stopped or
        stayed he,
But with mien of lord or lady, perched above my chamber door.

In the two stanzas which follow, the design is more obviously carried out:—

Then this ebony bird beguiling my sad fancy into smiling
By the *grave and stern decorum of the countenance it wore,*
"Though thy *crest be shorn and shaven* thou," I said, "art sure
        no craven,

Ghastly grim and ancient Raven wandering from the Nightly
       shore—
Tell me what thy lordly name is on the Night's Plutonian shore?"
       Quoth the Raven "Nevermore."

Much I marvelled *this ungainly fowl* to hear discourse so plainly
Though its answer little meaning—little relevancy bore;
For we cannot help agreeing that no living human being
Ever yet was blessed with seeing bird above his chamber door—
Bird or beast upon the sculptured bust above his chamber door,
       With such name as "Nevermore."

The effect of the *dénouement* being thus provided for, I immediately drop the fantastic for a tone of the most profound
seriousness:—this tone commencing in the stanza directly following the one last quoted, with the line,

But the Raven, sitting lonely on that placid bust, spoke only, etc.

From this epoch the lover no longer jests—no longer sees
any thing even of the fantastic in the Raven's demeanor. He
speaks of him as a "grim, ungainly, ghastly, gaunt, and ominous
bird of yore," and feels the "fiery eyes" burning into his "bosom's
core." This revolution of thought, or fancy, on the lover's part,
is intended to induce a similar one on the part of the reader—to
bring the mind into a proper frame for the *dénouement*—which
is now brought about as rapidly and as *directly* as possible.

With the *dénouement* proper—with the Raven's reply, "Nevermore," to the lover's final demand if he shall meet his mistress
in another world—the poem, in its obvious phase, that of a simple narrative, may be said to have its completion. So far, every
thing is within the limits of the accountable—of the real. A
raven, having learned by rote the single word "Nevermore,"
and having escaped from the custody of its owner, is driven at
midnight, through the violence of a storm, to seek admission at
a window from which a light still gleams—the chamber-window
of a student, occupied half in poring over a volume, half in
dreaming of a beloved mistress deceased. The casement being
thrown open at the fluttering of the bird's wings, the bird itself

perches on the most convenient seat out of the immediate reach of the student, who, amused by the incident and the oddity of the visitor's demeanor, demands of it, in jest and without looking for a reply, its name. The raven addressed, answers with its customary word, "Nevermore"—a word which finds immediate echo in the melancholy heart of the student, who, giving utterance aloud to certain thoughts suggested by the occasion, is again startled by the fowl's repetition of "Nevermore." The student now guesses the state of the case, but is impelled, as I have before explained, by the human thirst for self-torture, and in part by superstition, to propound such queries to the bird as will bring him, the lover, the most of the luxury of sorrow, through the anticipated answer "Nevermore." With the indulgence, to the extreme, of this self-torture, the narration, in what I have termed its first or obvious phase, has a natural termination, and so far there has been no overstepping of the limits of the real.

But in subjects so handled, however skilfully, or with however vivid an array of incident, there is always a certain hardness or nakedness, which repels the artistical eye. Two things are invariably required—first, some amount of complexity, or more properly, adaptation; and, secondly, some amount of suggestiveness—some under-current, however indefinite, of meaning. It is this latter, in especial, which imparts to a work of art so much of that *richness* (to borrow from colloquy a forcible term) which we are too fond of confounding with *the ideal*. It is the *excess* of the suggested meaning—it is the rendering this the upper instead of the under current of the theme—which turns into prose (and that of the very flattest kind) the so called poetry of the so called transcendentalists.

Holding these opinions, I added the two concluding stanzas of the poem—their suggestiveness being thus made to pervade all the narrative which has preceded them. The under-current of meaning is rendered first apparent in the lines—

"Take thy beak from out *my heart,* and take thy form from off
    my door!"
  Quoth the Raven "Nevermore!"

It will be observed that the words, "from out my heart," involve the first metaphorical expression in the poem. They, with the answer, "Nevermore," dispose the mind to seek a moral in all that has been previously narrated. The reader begins now to regard the Raven as emblematical—but it is not until the very last line of the very last stanza, that the intention of making him emblematical of *Mournful and Never-ending Remembrance* is permitted distinctly to be seen:

And the Raven, never flitting, still is sitting, still is sitting,
On the pallid bust of Pallas, just above my chamber door;
And his eyes have all the seeming of a demon's that is dreaming,
And the lamplight o'er him streaming throws his shadow on the
        floor;
And my soul *from out that shadow* that lies floating on the floor
        Shall be lifted—nevermore.

THE POETIC PRINCIPLE

In SPEAKING of the Poetic Principle, I have no design to be either thorough or profound. While discussing, very much at random, the essentiality of what we call Poetry, my principal purpose will be to cite for consideration, some few of those minor English or American poems which best suit my own taste, or which, upon my own fancy, have left the most definite impression. By "minor poems" I mean, of course, poems of little length. And here, in the beginning, permit me to say a few words in regard to a somewhat peculiar principle, which, whether rightfully or wrongfully, has always had its influence in my own critical estimate of the poem. I hold that a long poem does not exist. I maintain that the phrase, "a long poem," is simply a flat contradiction in terms.

I need scarcely observe that a poem deserves its title only inasmuch as it excites, by elevating the soul. The value of the poem is in the ratio of this elevating excitement. But all excitements are, through a psychal necessity, transient. That degree of excitement which would entitle a poem to be so called at all, cannot be sustained throughout a composition of any great length. After the lapse of half an hour, at the very utmost, it flags—fails—a revulsion ensues—and then the poem is, in effect, and in fact, no longer such.

There are, no doubt, many who have found difficulty in reconciling the critical dictum that the *Paradise Lost* is to be devoutly admired throughout, with the absolute impossibility of maintaining for it, during perusal, the amount of enthusiasm which that critical dictum would demand. This great work, in fact, is to be regarded as poetical, only when, losing sight of that vital requisite in all works of Art, Unity, we view it merely as a series of minor poems. If, to preserve its Unity—its totality of effect or impression—we read it (as would be necessary) at a single sitting, the result is but a constant alternation of excitement and depression. After a passage of what we feel to be true poetry, there follows, inevitably, a passage of platitude which no critical pre-judgment can force us to admire; but if, upon completing the work, we read it again; omitting the first book—that is to say, commencing with the second—we shall be surprised at now finding that admirable which we before condemned—that damnable which we had previously so much admired. It follows from all this that the ultimate, aggregate, or absolute effect of even the best epic under the sun, is a nullity:—and this is precisely the fact.

In regard to the Iliad, we have, if not positive proof, at least very good reason, for believing it intended as a series of lyrics; but, granting the epic intention, I can say only that the work is based in an imperfect sense of art. The modern epic is, of the supposititious ancient model, but an inconsiderate and blindfold imitation. But the day of these artistic anomalies is over. If, at any time, any very long poem *were* popular in reality, which I doubt, it is at least clear that no very long poem will ever be popular again.

That the extent of a poetical work is, *ceteris paribus*, the measure of its merit, seems undoubtedly, when we thus state it, a proposition sufficiently absurd—yet we are indebted for it to

129

the Quarterly Reviews. Surely there can be nothing in mere *size*, abstractly considered—there can be nothing in mere *bulk*, so far as a volume is concerned, which has so continuously elicited admiration from these saturnine pamphlets! A mountain, to be sure, by the mere sentiment of physical magnitude which it conveys, *does* impress us with a sense of the sublime—but no man is impressed after *this* fashion by the material grandeur of even *The Columbiad*. Even the Quarterlies have not instructed us to be so impressed by it. *As yet*, they have not *insisted* on our estimating Lamartine by the cubic foot, or Pollok by the pound— but what else are we to *infer* from their continual prating about "sustained effort"? If, by "sustained effort," any little gentleman has accomplished an epic, let us frankly commend him for the effort—if this indeed be a thing commendable—but let us forbear praising the epic on the effort's account. It is to be hoped that common sense, in the time to come, will prefer deciding upon a work of art, rather by the impression it makes, by the effect it produces, than by the time it took to impress the effect or by the amount of "sustained effort" which had been found necessary in effecting the impression. The fact is, that perseverance is one thing, and genius quite another—nor can all the Quarterlies in Christendom confound them. By-and-by, this proposition, with many which I have been just urging, will be received as self-evident. In the meantime, by being generally condemned as falsities, they will not be essentially damaged as truths.

On the other hand, it is clear that a poem may be improperly brief. Undue brevity degenerates into mere epigrammatism. A *very* short poem, while now and then producing a brilliant or vivid, never produces a profound or enduring effect. There must be the steady pressing down of the stamp upon the wax. De Béranger has wrought innumerable things, pungent and spirit-stirring; but, in a general, they have been too imponderous to stamp themselves deeply into the public attention; and thus, as so many feathers of fancy, have been blown aloft only to be whistled down the wind.

While the epic mania—while the idea that, to merit in poetry, prolixity is indispensable—has, for some years past, been gradually dying out of the public mind, by mere dint of its own absurdity—we find it succeeded by a heresy too palpably false to be long tolerated, but one which, in the brief period it has already endured, may be said to have accomplished more in the corruption of our Poetical Literature than all its other enemies combined. I allude to the heresy of *The Didactic*. It has been assumed, tacitly and avowedly, directly and indirectly, that the ultimate object of all Poetry is Truth. Every poem, it is said, should inculcate a moral; and by this moral is the poetical merit of the work to be adjudged. We Americans especially have patronised this happy idea; and we Bostonians, very especially, have developed it in full. We have taken it into our heads that to write a poem simply for the poem's sake, and to acknowledge such to have been our design, would be to confess ourselves radically wanting in the true Poetic dignity and force:—but the simple fact is, that, would we but permit ourselves to look into our own souls, we should immediately there discover that under the sun there neither exists nor *can* exist any work more thoroughly dignified—more supremely noble than this very poem— this poem *per se*—this poem which is a poem and nothing more —this poem written solely for the poem's sake.

With as deep a reverence for the True as ever inspired the bosom of man, I would, nevertheless, limit, in some measure, its modes of inculcation. I would limit to enforce them. I would not enfeeble them by dissipation. The demands of Truth are severe. She has no sympathy with the myrtles. All *that* which is so indispensable in Song, is precisely all *that* with which *she* has nothing whatever to do. It is but making her a flaunting paradox, to wreathe her in gems and flowers. In enforcing a truth, we need severity rather than efflorescence of language. We must be cool, calm, unimpassioned. In a word, we must be in that mood which, as nearly as possible, is the exact converse of the poetical. *He* must be blind, indeed, who does not perceive the radical and chasmal differences between the truthful and the poetical modes of inculcation. He must be theory-mad beyond redemption who, in spite of these differences, shall still persist in attempting to reconcile the obstinate oils and waters of Poetry and Truth.

Dividing the world of mind into its three most immediately obvious distinctions, we have the Pure Intellect, Taste, and the Moral Sense. I place Taste in the middle, because it is just this position which, in the mind, it occupies. It holds intimate relations with either extreme; but from the Moral Sense is separated by so faint a difference that Aristotle has not hesitated to place some of its operations among the virtues themselves. Nevertheless, we find the *offices* of the trio marked with a sufficient distinction. Just as the Intellect concerns itself with Truth, so Taste informs us of the Beautiful while the Moral Sense is regardful of Duty. Of this latter, while Conscience teaches the obligation, and Reason the expediency, Taste contents herself with displaying the charms:—waging war upon Vice solely on the ground of her deformity—her disproportion—her animosity to the fitting, to the appropriate, to the harmonious—in a word, to Beauty.

An immortal instinct, deep within the spirit of man, is thus, plainly, a sense of the Beautiful. This it is which administers to his delight in the manifold forms, and sounds, and odours, and sentiments amid which he exists. And just as the lily is repeated in the lake, or the eyes of Amaryllis in the mirror, so is the mere oral or written repetition of these forms, and sounds, and colours, and odours, and sentiments, a duplicate source of delight. But this mere repetition is not poetry. He who shall simply sing, with however glowing enthusiasm, or with however vivid a truth of description, of the sights, and sounds, and odours, and colours, and sentiments, which greet *him* in common with all mankind—he, I say, has yet failed to prove his divine title. There is still a something in the distance which he has been unable to attain. We have still a thirst unquenchable, to allay which he has not shown us the crystal springs. This thirst belongs to the immortality of Man. It is at once a consequence and an indication of his perennial existence. It is the desire of the moth for the star. It is no mere appreciation of the Beauty before us—but a wild effort to reach the Beauty above. Inspired by an ecstatic prescience of the glories beyond the grave, we struggle, by multiform combinations among the things and thoughts of Time, to attain a portion of that Loveliness whose very elements, perhaps, appertain to eternity alone. And thus when by Poetry—or when by Music, the most entrancing of the Poetic moods—we find ourselves melted into tears—we weep then—not as the Abbate Gravina supposes—through excess of pleasure, but through a certain, petulant, impatient sorrow at our inability to grasp *now*, wholly, here on earth, at once and for ever, those divine and rapturous joys, of which *through* the poem, or *through* the music, we attain to but brief and indeterminate glimpses.

The struggle to apprehend the supernal Loveliness—this struggle, on the part of souls fittingly constituted—has given to the world all *that* which it (the world) has ever been enabled at once to understand and *to feel* as poetic.

The Poetic Sentiment, of course, may develope itself in various modes—in Painting, in Sculpture, in Architecture, in the Dance—very especially in Music—and very peculiarly, and with a wide field, in the composition of the Landscape Garden. Our present theme, however, has regard only to its manifestation in words. And here let me speak briefly on the topic of rhythm. Contenting myself with the certainty that Music, in its various modes of metre, rhythm, and rhyme, is of so vast a moment in Poetry as never to be wisely rejected—is so vitally important an adjunct, that he is simply silly who declines its assistance, I will not now pause to maintain its absolute essentiality. It is in Music, perhaps, that the soul most nearly attains the great end for which, when inspired by the Poetic Sentiment, it struggles— the creation of supernal Beauty. It *may* be, indeed, that here this sublime end is, now and then, attained *in fact*. We are often made to feel, with a shivering delight, that from an earthly harp are stricken notes which *cannot* have been unfamiliar to the angels. And thus there can be little doubt that in the union of Poetry with Music in its popular sense, we shall find the widest field for the Poetic development. The old Bards and Minnesingers had advantages which we do not possess—and Thomas Moore, singing his own songs, was, in the most legitimate manner, perfecting them as poems.

To recapitulate, then:—I would define, in brief, the Poetry of words as *The Rhythmical Creation of Beauty*. Its sole arbiter is Taste. With the Intellect or with the Conscience, it has only collateral relations. Unless incidentally, it has no concern whatever either with Duty or with Truth.

A few words, however, in explanation. *That* pleasure which is at once the most pure, the most elevating, and the most intense, is derived, I maintain, from the contemplation of the Beautiful. In the contemplation of Beauty we alone find it possible to attain that pleasurable elevation, or excitement, *of the soul*, which we recognise as the Poetic Sentiment, and which is so easily distinguished from Truth, which is the satisfaction of the Reason, or from Passion, which is the excitement of the heart. I make Beauty, therefore—using the word as inclusive of the sublime—I make Beauty the province of the poem, simply because it is an obvious rule of Art that effects should be made to spring as directly as possible from their causes:—no one as yet having been weak enough to deny that the peculiar elevation in question is at least *most readily* attainable in the poem. It by no means follows, however, that the incitements of Passion, or the precepts of Duty, or even the lessons of Truth, may not be introduced into a poem, and with advantage, for they may subserve, incidentally, in various ways, the general purposes of the work:—but the true artist will always contrive to tone them down in proper subjection to that *Beauty* which is the atmosphere and the real essence of the poem.

Thus, although in a very cursory and imperfect manner, I have endeavoured to convey to you my conception of the Poetic Principle. It has been my purpose to suggest that, while this Principle itself is, strictly and simply, the Human Aspiration for Supernal Beauty, the manifestation of the Principle is always found in *an elevating excitement of the Soul*—quite independent of that passion which is the intoxication of the Heart—or of that Truth which is the satisfaction of the Reason. For, in regard to Passion, alas! its tendency is to degrade, rather than to elevate the Soul. Love, on the contrary—Love—the true, the divine Eros—the Uranian, as distinguished from the Dionaean Venus —is unquestionably the purest and truest of all poetical themes. And in regard to Truth—if, to be sure, through the attainment of a truth, we are led to perceive a harmony where none was apparent before, we experience, at once, the true poetical effect —but this effect is referable to the harmony alone, and not in the least degree to the truth which merely served to render the harmony manifest.

We shall reach, however, more immediately a distinct conception of what the true Poetry is, by mere reference to a few of the simple elements which induce in the Poet himself the true poetical effect. He recognises the ambrosia which nourishes his soul, in the bright orbs that shine in Heaven—in the volutes of the flower—in the clustering of low shrubberies—in the waving of the grain-fields—in the slanting of tall, Eastern trees—in the blue distance of mountains—in the grouping of clouds—in the twinkling of half-hidden brooks—in the gleaming of silver rivers —in the repose of sequestered lakes—in the star-mirroring depths of lonely wells. He perceives it in the songs of birds—in the harp of AEolus—in the sighing of the night-wind—in the repining voice of the forest—in the surf that complains to the shore—in the fresh breath of the woods—in the scent of the violet—in the voluptuous perfume of the hyacinth—in the suggestive odour that comes to him, at eventide, from far-distant, undiscovered islands, over dim oceans, illimitable and unexplored. He owns it in all noble thoughts—in all unworldly motives—in all holy impulses—in all chivalrous, generous, and self-sacrificing deeds. He feels it in the beauty of woman—in the grace of her step—in the lustre of her eye—in the melody of her voice—in her soft laughter—in her sigh—in the harmony of the rustling of her robes. He deeply feels it in her winning endearments—in her burning enthusiasms—in her gentle charities—in her meek and devotional endurances—but above all— ah, far above all—he kneels to it—he worships it in the faith, in the purity, in the strength, in the altogether divine majesty— of her *love*.

WILLIAM ELLERY CHANNING

IN SPEAKING of Mr. William Ellery Channing, who has just published a very neat little volume of poems, we feel the necessity of employing the indefinite rather than the definite article. He is *a*, and by no means *the*, William Ellery Channing. He is only *the son* of the great essayist deceased. He is just such a person, in despite of his *clarum et venerabile nomen*, as Pindar would have designated by the significant term τις. It may be said in his favor that nobody ever heard of him. Like an honest woman, he has always succeeded in keeping himself from being made the subject of gossip. His book contains about sixty-three things, which he calls poems, and which he no doubt seriously supposes so to be. They are full of all kinds of mistakes, of which the most important is that of their having been printed at all. They are not precisely English—nor will we insult a great nation by calling them Kickapoo; perhaps they are Channingese. We may convey some general idea of them by two foreign terms not in common use—the Italian *pavoneggiarsi*, "to strut like a peacock," and the German word for "sky-rocketing," *schwarmerei*. They are more preposterous, in a word, than any poems except those of the author of "Sam Patch"; for we presume we are right (are we not?) in taking it for granted that the author of "Sam Patch" is the very worst of all the wretched poets that ever existed upon earth.

In spite, however, of the customary phrase about a man's "making a fool of himself," we doubt if any one was ever a fool of his own free will and accord. A poet, therefore, should not always be taken too strictly to task. He should be treated with leniency, and, even when damned, should be damned with respect. Nobility of descent, too, should be allowed its privileges not more in social life than in letters. The son of a great author cannot be handled too tenderly by the critical Jack Ketch. Mr. Channing must be hung, that's true. He must be hung *in terrorem*—and for this there is no help under the sun; but then we shall do him all manner of justice, and observe every species of decorum, and be especially careful of his feelings, and hang him gingerly and gracefully, with a silken cord, as the Spaniards hang their grandees of the blue blood, their nobles of the *sangre azula.*

To be serious, then; as we always wish to be if possible. Mr. Channing (whom we suppose to be a *very* young man, since we are precluded from supposing him a *very* old one,) appears to have been inoculated, at the same moment, with *virus* from Tennyson and from Carlyle. And here we do not wish to be misunderstood. For Tennyson, as for a man imbued with the richest and rarest poetic impulses, we have an admiration—a reverence unbounded. His "Morte D'Arthur," his "Locksley Hall," his "Sleeping Beauty," his "Lady of Shalott," his "Lotos Eaters," his "AEnone," and many other poems, are not surpassed, in all that gives to Poetry its distinctive value, by the compositions of any one living or dead. And his leading error—that error which renders him unpopular—a point, to be sure, of no particular importance—that very error, we say, is founded in truth—in a keen perception of the elements of poetic beauty. We allude to his quaintness—to what the world chooses to term his affectation. No true poet—no critic whose approbation is worth even a copy of the volume we now hold in our hand—will deny that he feels impressed, sometimes even to tears, by many of those very affectations which he is impelled by the prejudice of his education, or by the cant of his reason, to condemn. He should thus be led to examine the extent of the one, and to be wary of the deductions of the other. In fact, the profound intuition of Lord Bacon has supplied, in one of his immortal apothegms, the whole philosophy of the point at issue. "There is no exquisite beauty," he truly says, "without some *strangeness* in its proportions." We maintain, then, that Tennyson errs, not in his occasional quaintness, but in its continual and obtrusive excess. And, in accusing Mr. Channing of having been inoculated with *virus* from Tennyson, we merely mean to say that he has adopted and exaggerated that noble poet's characteristic defect, having mistaken it for his principal merit.

Mr. Tennyson is quaint only; he is never, as some have supposed him, obscure—except, indeed, to the uneducated, whom he does not address. Mr. Carlyle, on the other hand, is obscure only; he is seldom, as some have imagined him, quaint. So far he is right; for although quaintness, employed by a man of judgment and genius, may be made auxiliary to a *poem*, whose true thesis is beauty, and beauty alone, it is grossly, and even ridiculously, out of place in a work of prose. But in his obscurity it is scarcely necessary to say that he is wrong. Either a man intends to be understood, or he does not. If he write a book which he intends *not* to be understood, we shall be very happy indeed not to understand it; but if he write a book which he means to be understood, and, in this book, be at all possible pains to prevent us from understanding it, we can only say that he is an ass—and this, to be brief, is our private opinion of Mr. Carlyle, which we now take the liberty of making public.

It seems that having deduced, from Tennyson and Carlyle, an opinion of the sublimity of everything odd, and of the pro-fundity of everything meaningless, Mr. Channing has conceived the idea of setting up for himself as a poet of *unusual* depth, and *very* remarkable powers of mind. His airs and graces, in consequence, have a highly picturesque effect, and the Boston critics, who have a notion that poets are porpoises, (for they are always talking about their running in "schools,") cannot make up their minds as to what particular school he must belong. *We* say the Bobby Button school, by all means. He clearly belongs to that. And should nobody ever have heard of the Bobby Button school, that is a point of no material importance. We will answer for it, as it is one of our own. Bobby Button is a gentleman with whom, for a long time, we have had the honor of an intimate acquaintance. His personal appearance is striking. He has quite a big head. His eyes protrude and have all the air of saucers. His chin retreats. His mouth is depressed at the corners. He wears a perpetual frown of contemplation. His words are slow, emphatic, few, and oracular. His "thes," "ands," and "buts," have more meaning than other men's polysyllables. His nods would have put Burleigh's to the blush. His whole aspect, indeed, conveys the idea of a gentleman modest to a fault, and painfully overburthened with intellect. We insist, however, upon calling Mr. Channing's school of poetry the Bobby Button school, rather because Mr. Channing's poetry is strongly suggestive of Bobby Button, than because Mr. Button himself ever dallied, to any very great extent, with the Muses. With the exception, indeed, of a *very* fine "Sonnet to a Pig"—or rather the fragment of a sonnet, for he proceeded no farther than the words "O piggy wiggy," with the O italicized for emphasis—with the exception of this, we say, we are not aware of his having produced anything worthy of that stupendous genius which is certainly *in* him, and only wants, like the starling of Sterne, "to get out."

The best passage in the book before us, is to be found at page 121, and we quote it, as a matter of simple justice, in full:

> Dear friend, in this fair atmosphere again,
> Far from the noisy echoes of the main,
> Amid the world-old mountains, and the hills
> From whose strange grouping a fine power distills
> The soothing and the calm, I seek repose,
> The city's noise forgot and hard stern woes.
> As thou once said'st, the rarest sons of earth
> Have in the dust of cities shown their worth,
> Where long collision with the human curse
> Has of great glory been the frequent nurse,
> *And only those who in sad cities dwell*
> *Are of the green trees fully sensible.*
> *To them the silver bells of tinkling streams*
> *Seem brighter than an angel's laugh in dreams.*

The four lines italicized are highly meritorious, and the whole extract is so far decent and intelligible, that we experienced a feeling of surprise upon meeting it amid the doggerel which surrounds it. Not less was our astonishment upon finding, at page 18, a fine thought so well embodied as the following:

> *Or see the early stars, a mild sweet train.*
> *Come out to bury the diurnal sun.*

But, in the way of commendation, we have now done. We have carefully explored the whole volume in vain, for a single additional line worth even the most qualified applause.

The utter *abandon*—the charming *negligé*—the perfect loose-ness (to use a western phrase) of his rhythm, is one of Mr. C.'s most noticeable, and certainly one of his most refreshing traits. It would be quite a pleasure to hear him read or scan, or to hear anybody else read or scan, such a line as this, at page 3, for example:

> Masculine almost though softly carv'd in grace,

where "masculine" has to be read as a trochee, and "almost" as an iambus; or this, at page 8:

> That compels me on through wood, and fell, and moor,

where "that compels" has to be pronounced as equivalent to the iambus "me on"; or this, at page 18:

> I leave thee, *the* maid spoke to *the* true youth,

where both the *"thes"* demand a strong accent to preserve the iambic rhythm; or this, at page 29:

> So in our steps strides truth and honest trust,

where (to say nothing of the grammar, which *may* be Dutch, but is not English) it is quite impossible to get through with the "steps strides truth" without dislocating the under jaw; or this, at page 32:

> The serene azure *the* keen stars are now;

or this, on the same page:

> Sometimes of sorrow, joy, to *thy* Future;

or this, at page 56:

> *Harsh action, even in repose inwardly harsh;*

* * *

At page 136, we read as follows:

> Tune thy clear voice to no funereal song,
> *For O Death stands to welcome thee sure.*

At page 116, he has this:

> ————These graves, you mean;
> Their history who knows bet*ter* than I?
> For in the busy street strikes on my ear
> *Each sound, even inaudible voices*
> Lengthen the long tale my memory tells.

Just below, on the same page, he has

> I see but little difference tru*ly;*

and at page 76 he fairly puts the climax to metrical absurdity in the lines which follow:

> The spirit builds his house in *the* last flowers—
> A beautiful mansion; how the colors live.
> In*tr*icately de*l*icate!

This is to be read, of course, intrikkittly delikkit, and "intrikkittly delikkit" it is —unless, indeed, we are very especially mistaken.

The affectations—the Tennysonisms of Mr. Channing—pervade his book at all points, and are not easily particularized. He employs, for example, the word "delight" for "delighted"; as at page 2:

> Delight to trace the mountain-brook's descent.

He uses, also, all the prepositions in a different sense from the rabble. If, for instance, he was called upon to say "on," he wouldn't say it by any means, but he'd say "off," and endeavor to make it answer the purpose. For "to," in the same manner, he says "from"; for "with," "of," and so on: at page 2, for example:

Nor less in winter, mid the glittering banks
Heaped *of* unspotted snow, the maiden roved.

For "serene," he says "*serene*"; as at page 4:

The influences of this *serene* isle.

* * *

Instead of "more infinite," he writes "infi*nit*er," with an accent
on the "nit," as thus, at page 100:

Hope's child, I summon infi*nit*er powers.

And here we might as well ask Mr. Channing, in passing, what
idea he attaches to infinity, and whether he really thinks that
he is at liberty to subject the adjective "infinite" to degrees of
comparison. Some of these days we shall hear, no doubt, of
"eternal, eternaler, and eternalest."

Our author is quite enamoured of the word "sumptuous,"
and talks about "sumptuous trees" and "sumptuous girls," with
no other object, we think, than to employ the epithet at all
hazards and upon all occasions. He seems unconscious that it
means nothing more than expensive, or costly; and we are not
quite sure that either trees or girls are, in America, either the
one or the other.

For "loved" Mr. C. prefers to say "was loving," and takes
great pleasure in the law phrase "the same." Both peculiarities
are exemplified at page 20, where he says:

The maid was loving this enamoured same.

He is fond also, of inversions and contractions, and employs
them in a very singular manner. At page 15 he has:

Now may I thee describe a Paradise

At page 86 he says:

Thou lazy river, flowing neither way
Me figurest and yet thy banks seem gay.

142

At page 143 he writes:

> Men change that Heaven above not more;

meaning that men change so much that Heaven above does not change more. At page 150 he says:

> But so much soul hast thou within thy form
> Than luscious summer days thou art the more

by which he would imply that the lady has so much soul within her form that she is more luscious than luscious summer days.

* * *

At page 102, he has the following:—

> Dry leaves with yellow ferns, they are
> Fit wreath of Autumn, while a star
> Still, bright, and pure, our frosty air
> Shivers in twinkling points
> Of thin celestial hair
> And thus one side of Heaven anoints.

This we think we can explain. Let us see. Dry leaves, mixed with yellow ferns, are a wreath fit for autumn at the time when our frosty air shivers a still, bright, and pure star with twinkling points of thin celestial hair, and with this hair, or hair plaster, anoints one side of the sky. Yes—this is it—no doubt.

At page 123, we have these lines:

> My sweet girl is lying still
> In her lovely atmosphere;
> The gentle hopes her blue veins fill
> With pure silver warm and clear.
>
> O see her hair, O mark her breast!
> Would it not, O! comfort thee,
> If thou couldst nightly go to rest
> By that virgin chastity?

Yes; we think, upon the whole, it would. The eight lines are entitled a "Song," and we should like very much to hear Mr. Channing sing it.

Pages 36, 37, 38, 39, 40, and 41, are filled with short "Thoughts" in what Mr. C. supposes to be the manner of Jean Paul. One of them runs thus:

> How shall I live? In earnestness.
> What shall I do? Work earnestly.
> What shall I give? A willingness.
> What shall I gain? Tranquility.
> But do you mean a quietness
> In which I act and no man bless?
> Flash out in action infinite and free,
> Action conjoined with deep tranquility,
> Resting upon the soul's true utterance,
> And life shall flow as merry as a dance.

All our readers will be happy to hear, we are sure, that Mr. C. is going "to flash out." Elsewhere at page 97, he expresses very similar sentiments:

> My empire is myself and I dyfy
> The external; yes, I rule the whole or die.

It will be observed here, that Mr. Channing's empire is himself, (a small kingdom, however,) that he intends to defy "the external," whatever that is—perhaps he means the infernals—and that, in short, he is going to rule the whole or die; all which is very proper, indeed, and nothing more than we have to expect from Mr. C.

Again, at page 146, he is rather fierce than otherwise. He says:

> We surely were not meant to ride the sea,
>   Skimming the wave in that so prisoned small,
> Reposing our infinite faculties utterly.
>   Boom like a roaring sunlit waterfall.
> Humming to infinite abysms: speak loud, speak free!

Here Mr. Channing not only intends to "speak loud and free" himself, but advises every body else to do likewise. For his own part, he says, he is going to *"boom"*—"to hum and to boom"— to "hum like a roaring waterfall," and "boom to an infinite abysm." What, in the name of Belzebub, *is* to become of us all?

* * *

And this remarkable little volume is, after all, by William Ellery Channing. A great name it has been said, is, in many cases, a great misfortune. We hear daily complaints from the George Washington Dixons, the Socrates Smiths, and the Napoleon Buonaparte Joneses, about the inconsiderate ambition of their parents and sponsors. By inducing invidious comparison, these *proenomina* get their bearers (so they say) into every variety of scrape. If George Washington Dixon, for example, does not think proper, upon compulsion, to distinguish himself as a patriot, he is considered a very singular man; and Socrates Smith is never brought up before his honor the Mayor without receiving a double allowance of thirty days; while his honor the Mayor can assign no sounder reason for his serevity, than that better things than getting toddied are to be expected of Socrates. Napoleon Buonaparte Jones, on the other hand, to say nothing of being called Nota Bene Jones by all his acquaintance, is cow-skinned, with perfect regularity, five times a month, merely because people *will* feel it a point of honor to cowskin a Napoleon Buonaparte.

And yet these gentlemen—the Smiths and the Joneses—are wrong *in toto*—as the Smiths and the Joneses invariably are. They are wrong, we say, in accusing their parents and sponsors. They err in attributing their misfortunes and persecutions to the *proenomina*—to the names assigned them at the baptismal font. Mr. Socrates Smith does not receive his double quantum of thirty days because he is called Socrates, but because he is called Socrates *Smith*. Mr. Napoleon Buonaparte Jones is not in the weekly receipt of a flogging on account of being Mr. Napoleon Buonaparte, but simply on account of being Mr. Napoleon Buonaparte *Jones*. Here, indeed, is a clear distinction. It is the surname which is to blame, after all. Mr. Smith must drop the Smith. Mr. Jones should discard the Jones. No one would ever think of taking Socrates—Socrates solely—to the watchhouse; and there is not a bully living who would venture to cowskin Napoleon Buonaparte *per se*. . . . But no such ingenuity has been needed in the case of Mr. William Ellery Channing, who has been befriended by Fate, or the foresight of his sponsors, and who has *no* Jones or Smith at the end of his name.

And here, too, a question occurs. . . . There are a vast number of uninformed young persons prowling about our bookshops, who will be raw enough to buy, and even to read half through this pretty little book, (God preserve and forgive them!) mistaking it for the composition of another. But what then? Are not books made, as well as razors, to sell? The poet's name *is* William Ellery Channing—is it *not?* And if a man has not a right to the use of his own name, to the use of what has he a right? And could the poet have reconciled it to his conscience to have injured the sale of his own volume by any uncalled-for announcement upon the title-page, or in a preface, to the effect that he is not his father, but only his father's very intelligent son? To put the case more clearly by reference to our old friends, Mr. Smith and Mr. Jones. Is either Mr. Smith, when mistaken for Socrates, or Mr. Jones, when accosted as Napoleon, bound, by any conceivable species of honor, to inform the whole world —the one, that he is not Socrates, but only Socrates Smith; the other, that he is by no means Napoleon Buonaparte, but only Napoleon Buonaparte Jones?

I HAVE sometimes amused myself by endeavoring to fancy what would be the fate of any individual gifted, or rather accursed, with an intellect *very* far superior to that of his race. Of course, he would be conscious of his superiority; nor could he (if otherwise constituted as man is) help manifesting his consciousness. Thus he would make himself enemies at all points. And since his opinions and speculations would widely differ from those of *all* mankind—that he would be considered a madman, is evident. How horribly painful such a condition! Hell could invent no greater torture than that of being charged with abnormal weakness on account of being abnormally strong.

In like manner, nothing can be clearer than that a *very* generous spirit—*truly* feeling what all merely profess—must inevitably find itself misconceived in every direction—its motives misinterpreted. Just as extremeness of intelligence would be thought fatuity, so excess of chivalry could not fail of being looked upon as meanness in its last degree:—and so on with other virtues. This subject is a painful one indeed. That individuals *have* so soared above the plane of their race, is scarcely to be questioned; but, in looking back through history for traces of their existence, we should pass over all biographies of "the good and the great," while we search carefully the slight records of wretches who died in prison, in Bedlam, or upon the gallows.

IF ANY ambitious man have a fancy to revolutionize, at one effort, the universal world of human thought, human opinion, and human sentiment, the opportunity is his own—the road to immortal renown lies straight, open, and unencumbered before him. All that he has to do is to write and publish a very little book—*My Heart Laid Bare*. But—this little book must be *true to its title*.

Now, is it not very singular that, with the rabid thirst for notoriety which distinguishes so many of mankind—so many, too, who care not a fig what is thought of them after death, there should not be found one man having sufficient hardihood to write this little book? To *write*, I say. There are ten thousand men who, if the book were once written, would laugh at the notion of being disturbed by its publication during their life, and who could not even conceive *why* they should object to its being published after their death. But to write it—*there* is the rub. No man dare write it. No man ever will dare write it. No man *could* write it, even if he dared. The paper would shrivel and blaze at every touch of the fiery pen.

MEN OF GENIUS are far more abundant than is supposed. In fact, to appreciate thoroughly the work of what we call genius, is to possess all the genius by which the work was produced. But the person appreciating may be utterly incompetent to reproduce the work, or any thing similar, and this solely through lack of what may be termed the constructive ability—a matter quite independent of what we agree to understand in the term "genius" itself. This ability is based, to be sure, in great part, upon the faculty of analysis, enabling the artist to get full view of the machinery of his proposed effect, and thus work it and regulate it at will; but a great deal depends also upon properties strictly moral—for example, upon patience, upon concentrativeness, or the power of holding the attention steadily to the one purpose, upon self-dependence and contempt for all opinion which is opinion and no more—in especial, upon energy or industry. So vitally important is this last, that it may well be doubted if any thing to which we have been accustomed to give the title of a "work of genius" was ever accomplished without it; and it is chiefly because this quality and genius are nearly incompatible, that "works of genius" are few, while mere men of genius are, as I say, abundant. The Romans, who excelled us in acuteness of *observation*, while falling below us in induction from facts observed, seem to have been so fully aware of the inseparable connection between industry and a "work of genius" as to have adopted the error that industry, in great measure, was genius itself. The highest compliment is intended by a Roman when, of an epic, or any thing similar, he says that it is written *industriâ mirabili* or *incredibili industriâ*.

AN EXCELLENT magazine paper might be written upon the subject of the progressive steps by which any great work of art—especially of literary art—attained completion. How vast a dissimilarity always exists between the germ and the fruit—between the work and its original conception! Sometimes the original conception is abandoned, or left out of sight altogether. Most authors sit down to write with *no* fixed design, trusting to the inspiration of the moment; it is not, therefore, to be wondered at, that *most* books are valueless. Pen should never touch paper, until at least a well-digested *general* purpose be established. In fiction, the *dénouement*—in all other composition the intended *effect*, should be definitely considered and arranged, before writing the first word; and no word should be then written which does not tend, or form a part of a sentence which tends to the development of the *dénouement*, or to the strengthening of the effect. Where *plot* forms a portion of the contemplated interest, too much preconsideration cannot be had. *Plot* is very imperfectly understood, and has never been rightly defined. Many persons regard it as mere complexity of incident. In its most rigorous acceptation, it is *that from which no component atom can be removed, and in which none of the component atoms can be displaced, without ruin to the whole;* and although a sufficiently good plot may be constructed, without attention to the whole rigor of this definition, still it is the definition which the true artist should always keep in view, and always endeavor to consummate in his works.

SOME FRENCHMAN—possibly Montaigne—says: "People talk about thinking, but for my part I never think, except when I sit down to write." It is this never thinking, unless when we sit down to write, which is the cause of so much indifferent composition. But perhaps there is something more involved in the Frenchman's observation than meets the eye. It is certain that the mere act of inditing, tends, in a great degree, to the logicalization of thought. Whenever, on account of its vagueness, I am dissatisfied with a conception of the brain, I resort forthwith to the pen, for the purpose of obtaining, through its aid, the necessary form, consequence and precision.

How very commonly we hear it remarked, that such and such thoughts are beyond the compass of words! I do not believe that any thought, properly so called, is out of the reach of language. I fancy, rather, that where difficulty in expression is experienced, there is, in the intellect which experiences it, a want either of deliberateness or of method. For my own part, I have never had a thought which I could not set down in words, with even more distinctness than that with which I conceived it:—as I have before observed, the thought is logicalized by the effort at (written) expression.

There is, however, a class of fancies, of exquisite delicacy, which are *not* thoughts, and to which, *as yet*, I have found it absolutely impossible to adapt language. I use the word *fancies* at random, and merely because I must use *some* word; but the idea commonly attached to the term is not even remotely applicable to the shadows of shadows in question. They seem to me rather psychal than intellectual. They arise in the soul (alas, how rarely!) only at its epochs of most intense tranquillity—when the bodily and mental health are in perfection—and at those mere points of time where the confines of the waking world blend with those of the world of dreams. I am aware of these "fancies" only when I am upon the very brink of sleep, with the consciousness that I am so. I have satisfied myself that this condition exists but for an inappreciable *point* of time—yet it is crowded with these "shadows of shadows"; and for absolute *thought* there is demanded time's *endurance*.

These "fancies" have in them a pleasurable ecstasy as far beyond the most pleasurable of the world of wakefulness, or of dreams, as the Heaven of the Northman theology is beyond its Hell. I regard the visions, even as they arise, with an awe which, in some measure, moderates or tranquilizes the ecstasy—I so regard them, through a conviction (which seems a portion of the ecstasy itself) that this ecstasy, in itself, is of a character supernal to the Human Nature—is a glimpse of the spirit's outer world; and I arrive at this conclusion—if this term is at all applicable to instantaneous intuition—by a perception that the delight experienced has, as its element, but *the absoluteness of novelty.* I say the absoluteness—for in these fancies—let me now term them psychal impressions—there is really nothing even approximate in character to impressions ordinarily received. It is as if the five senses were supplanted by five myriad others alien to mortality.

Now, so entire is my faith in the *power of words,* that, at times, I have believed it possible to embody even the evanescence of fancies such as I have attempted to describe. In experiments with this end in view, I have proceeded so far as, first, to control (when the bodily and mental health are good) the existence of the condition:—that is to say, I can now (unless when ill) be sure that the condition will supervene, if I so wish it, at the point of time already described: of its supervention, until lately, I could never be certain, even under the most favorable circumstances. I mean to say, merely, that now I can be sure, when all circumstances are favorable, of the supervention of the condition, and feel even the capacity of inducing or compelling it:—the favorable circumstances, however, are not the less rare —else had I compelled, already, the Heaven into the Earth.

I have proceeded so far, secondly, as to prevent the lapse from *the point* of which I speak—the point of blending between wakefulness and sleep—as to prevent at will, I say, the lapse from this border-ground into the dominion of sleep. Not that I can *continue* the condition—not that I can render the point more than a point—but that I can startle myself from the point into wakefulness—*and thus transfer the point itself into the realm of Memory*—convey its impressions, or more properly their recollections, to a situation where (although still for a very brief period) I can survey them with the eye of analysis.

For these reasons—that is to say, because I have been enabled to accomplish thus much—I do not altogether despair of embodying in words at least enough of the fancies in question to convey, to certain classes of intellect, a shadowy conception of their character.

In saying this I am not to be understood as supposing that the fancies, or psychal impressions, to which I allude, are confined to my individual self—are not, in a word, common to all

151

mankind—for on this point it is quite impossible that I should form an opinion—but nothing can be more certain than that even a partial record of the impressions would startle the universal intellect of mankind, by the *supremeness of the novelty* of the material employed, and of its consequent suggestions. In a word—should I ever write a paper on this topic, the world will be compelled to acknowledge that, at last, I have done an original thing.

THE EFFECT derivable from well-managed rhyme is very imperfectly understood. Conventionally "rhyme" implies merely close similarity of sound at the ends of verse, and it is really curious to observe how long mankind have been content with their limitation of the idea. What, in rhyme, first and principally pleases, may be referred to the human sense or appreciation of *equality*—the common element, as might be easily shown, of all the gratification we derive from music in its most extended sense —very especially in its modifications of metre and rhythm. We see, for example, a crystal, and are immediately interested by the equality between the sides and angles of one of its faces—but on bringing to view a second face, in all respects similar to our first, our pleasure seems to be *squared*—on bringing to view a third, it appears to be *cubed*, and so on: I have no doubt, indeed, that the delight experienced, if measurable, would be found to have exact mathematical relations, such, or nearly such, as I suggest—that is to say, as far as a certain point, beyond which there would be a decrease, in similar relations. Now here, as the ultimate result of analysis, we reach the sense of mere *equality*, or rather the human delight in this sense; and it was an instinct, rather than a clear comprehension of this delight as a principle, which, in the first instance, led the poet to attempt an increase of the effect arising from the mere similarity (that is to say equality) between two sounds—led him, I say, to attempt increasing this effect by making a secondary equalization, in placing the rhymes at equal distances—that is, at the ends of lines of equal length. In this manner, rhyme and the termination of the line grew connected in men's thoughts—grew into a conventionalism—the principle being lost sight of altogether. And it was simply because Pindaric verses had, before this epoch, existed—*i.e.* verses of unequal length—that rhymes were subsequently found at unequal distances. It was for this reason solely, I say—for none more profound—rhyme had come to be regarded as of right appertaining to the end of verse—and here we complain that the matter has finally rested.

But it is clear that there was much more to be considered. So far, the sense of equality alone, entered the effect; or, if this equality was slightly varied, it was varied only through an accident—the accident of the existence of Pindaric metres. It will be seen that the rhymes were always anticipated. The eye, catching the end of a verse, whether long or short, expected, for the ear, a rhyme. The great element of unexpectedness was not dreamed of—that is to say, of novelty—of originality. "But," says Lord Bacon, (how justly!) "there is no exquisite beauty without some strangeness in the proportions." Take away this element of strangeness—of unexpectedness—of novelty—of originality— call it what we will—and all that is ethereal in loveliness is lost at once. We lose—we miss the unknown—the vague—the uncomprehended, because offered before we have time to examine and comprehend. We lose, in short, all that assimilates the beauty of earth with what we dream of the beauty of Heaven.

Perfection of rhyme is attainable only in the combination of the two elements, Equality and Unexpectedness. But as evil cannot exist without good, so unexpectedness must arise from expectedness. We do not contend for mere arbitrariness of rhyme. In the first place, we must have equi-distant or regularly recurring rhymes, to form the basis, expectedness, out of which arises the element, unexpectedness, by the introduction of rhymes, not arbitrarily, but with an eye to the greatest amount of unexpectedness. We should not introduce them, for example, at such points that the entire line is a multiple of the syllables preceding the points. When, for instance, I write—

And the silken, sad, uncertain rustling of each purple curtain,

153

I produce more, to be sure, but not remarkably more than the ordinary effect of rhymes regularly recurring at the end of lines; for the number of syllables in the whole verse is merely a multiple of the number of syllables preceding the rhyme introduced at the middle, and there is still left, therefore, a certain degree of expectedness. What there is of the element unexpectedness, is addressed, in fact, to the eye only—for the ear divides the verse into two ordinary lines, thus—

> And the silken, sad, uncertain
> Rustling of each purple curtain.

I obtain, however, the whole effect of unexpectedness, when I write—

> *Thrilled* me, *filled* me with fantastic terrors never felt before.

N.B. It is very commonly supposed that rhyme, as it now ordinarily exists, is of modern invention—but see the "Clouds" of Aristophanes. Hebrew verse, however, did *not* include it—the terminations of the lines, where most distinct, never showing anything of the kind.

WERE IT POSSIBLE to throw into a bag the lofty thought and manner of the "Pilgrims of the Rhine," together with the quirks and quibbles and true humour of "Tristram Shandy," not forgetting a few of the heartier drolleries of Rabelais, and one or two of the Phantasy Pieces of the Lorrainean Callôt, the whole, when well shaken up, and thrown out, would be a very tolerable imitation of [Longfellow's] "Hyperion." This may appear to be commendation, but we do not intend it as such. Works like this of Professor Longfellow are the triumphs of Tom O'Bedlam, and the grief of all true criticism. They are potent in unsettling the popular faith in Art—a faith which, at no day more than the present, needed the support of men of letters. That such things succeed at all, is attributable to the sad fact that there exist men of genius who, now and then, unmindful of duty, indite them—

that men of genius *ever* indite them is attributable to the fact that these are often the most indolent of human beings. A man of true talent who would demur at the great labour requisite for the stern demands of high art—at the unremitting toil and patient elaboration which, when soul-guided, result in the beauty of Unity, Totality, Truth—men, we say, who would demur at such labour, make no scruple of scattering at random a profusion of rich thought in the pages of such farragos as "Hyperion." Here, indeed, there is little trouble—but even that little is most unprofitably lost. To the writers of these things we say —all Ethics lie, and all History lies, or the world shall forget ye and your *works*. We have no design of commenting, at any length, upon what Professor Longfellow has written. We are indignant that he too has been recreant to the good cause. We, therefore, dismiss his "Hyperion" in brief. We grant him high qualities, but deny him *the Future*. In the present instance, without design, without shape, without beginning, middle, or end, what earthly object has his book accomplished?—what definite impression has it left?

IF EVER mortal "wreaked his thoughts upon expression," it was *Shelley*. If ever poet sang—as a bird sings—earnestly—impulsively—with utter abandonment—to himself solely—and for the mere joy of his own song—that poet was the author of "The Sensitive Plant." Of art—beyond that which is instinctive with genius—he either had little or disdained all. He *really* disdained that Rule which is an emanation from Law, because his own soul was Law in itself. His rhapsodies are but the rough notes— the stenographic memoranda of poems—memoranda which, because they were all-sufficient for his own intelligence, he cared not to be at the trouble of writing out in full for mankind. In all his works we find no conception thoroughly wrought. For this reason he is the most fatiguing of poets. Yet he wearies in saying too little rather than too much. What in him seems the diffuseness of one idea, is the conglomerate concision of many: and this species of concision it is, which renders him obscure. With such a man, to imitate was out of the question. It would have served no purpose; for he spoke to his own spirit alone, which would have comprehended no alien tongue. Thus he was profoundly original. His quaintness arose from intuitive perception of that truth to which Bacon alone has given distinct utterance:—"There is no exquisite Beauty which has not some strangeness in its proportions." But whether obscure, original, or quaint, Shelley had no *affectations*. He was at all times sincere.

From his *ruins*, there sprang into existence, affronting the heavens, a tottering and fantastic *pagoda*, in which the salient angles, tipped with mad jangling bells, were the idiosyncratic *faults* of the original—faults which cannot be considered such in view of his purposes, but which are monstrous when we regard his works as addressed to mankind. A "school" arose—if that absurd term must still be employed—a school—a system of *rules* upon the basis of the Shelley who had none. Young men innumerable, dazzled with the glare and bewildered by the *bizarrerie* of the lightning that flickered through the clouds of "Alastor" had no trouble whatever in heaping up imitative vapors, but, for the lightning, were forced to be content with its *spectrum*, in which the *bizarrerie* appeared without the fire. Nor were mature minds unimpressed by the contemplation of a greater and more mature; and thus, gradually, into this school of all Lawlessness—of obscurity, quaintness and exaggeration— were interwoven the out-of-place didacticism of Wordsworth, and the more anomalous metaphysicianism of Coleridge. Matters were now fast verging to their worst; and at length, in *Tennyson* poetic inconsistency attained its extreme. But it was precisely this extreme (for the greatest truth and the greatest error are scarcely two points in a circle) which, following the law of all extremes, wrought in him (Tennyson) a natural and inevitable revulsion; leading him first to contemn, and secondly to investigate, his early manner, and finally to winnow, from its magnificent elements, the truest and purest of all poetical styles. But not even yet is the process complete; and for this reason in part, but chiefly on account of the mere fortuitousness of that mental and moral combination which shall unite in one person (if *ever* it shall) the Shellyan *abandon* and the Tenny-sonian poetic sense, with the most profound Art (based both in Instinct and *Analysis*) and the sternest Will properly to blend and rigorously to control all—chiefly, I say, because such combination of seeming antagonisms will be only a "happy chance" —the world has never yet seen the noblest poem which, possibly, *can* be composed.

I AM NOT sure that Tennyson is not the greatest of poets. The uncertainty attending the public conception of the term "poet" alone prevents me from demonstrating that he *is*. Other bards produce effects which are, now and then, otherwise produced than by what we call poems; but Tennyson an effect which only a poem does. His alone are idiosyncratic poems. By the enjoyment or nonenjoyment of the "Morte D'Arthur," or of the "AEnone," I would test any one's ideal sense. There are passages in his works which rivet a conviction I had long entertained, that the *indefinite* is an element in the true ποιησις. Why do some persons fatigue themselves in attempts to unravel such fantasy-pieces as the "Lady of Shalott?" As well unweave the *"ventum textilem."* If the author did not deliberately propose himself a suggestive indefinitiveness of meaning, with the view of bringing about a definitiveness of vague and therefore of spiritual *effect*—this, at least, arose from the silent analytical promptings of that poetic genius which, in its supreme development, embodies all orders of intellectual capacity. I *know* that indefinitiveness is an element of the true music—I mean of the true musical expression. Give to it any undue decision—imbue it with any very determinate tone—and you deprive it, at once, of its ethereal, its ideal, its intrinsic and essential character. You dispel its luxury of dream. You dissolve the atmosphere of the mystic upon which it floats. You exhaust it of its breath of fäery. It now becomes a tangible and easily appreciable idea— a thing of the earth, earthy. It has not, indeed, lost its power to please, but all which I consider the distinctiveness of that power. And to the uncultivated talent, or to the unimaginative apprehension, this deprivation of its most delicate nare will be, not unfrequently, a recommendation. A determinateness of expression is sought—and often by composers who should know better—is sought as a beauty rather than rejected as a blemish. Thus we have, even from high authorities, attempts at absolute *imitation* in music. Who can forget the silliness of the "Battle of Prague?" What man of taste but must laugh at the interminable drums, trumpets, blunderbusses, and thunder? . . . Tennyson's shorter pieces abound in minute rhythmical lapses sufficient to assure me that—in common with all poets living or dead—he has neglected to make precise investigation of the principles of metre; but, on the other hand, so perfect is his rhythmical instinct in general, that, like the present Viscount Canterbury, he seems *to see with his ear*.

ONE HALF the pleasure experienced at a theatre arises from the spectator's sympathy with the rest of the audience, and, especially, from his belief in their sympathy with him. The eccentric gentleman who not long ago, at the Park, found himself the solitary occupant of box, pit, and gallery, would have derived but little enjoyment from his visit, had he been suffered to remain. It was an act of mercy to turn him out. The present absurd rage for lecturing is founded in the feeling in question. Essays which we would not be hired to read—so trite is their subject—so feeble is their execution—so much easier is it to get better information on similar themes out of any encyclopaedia in Christendom—we are brought to tolerate, and alas, even to applaud in their tenth and twentieth repetition, through the sole force of our sympathy with the throng. In the same way we listen to a story with greater zest when there are others present at its narration beside ourselves. Aware of this, authors without due reflection have repeatedly attempted, by supposing a circle of listeners, to imbue their narratives with the interest of sympathy. At a cursory glance the idea seems plausible enough. But, in the one case, there is an actual, personal, and palpable sympathy, conveyed in looks, gestures and brief comments—a sympathy of real individuals, all with the matters discussed to be sure, but then especially, *each with each*. In the other instance, we, alone in our closet, are required to sympathise *with* the sympathy of fictitious listeners, who, so far from being present in body, are often studiously kept out of sight and out of mind for two or three hundred pages at a time. This is sympathy double-diluted—the shadow of a shade. It is unnecessary to say that the design invariably fails of its effect.

IN ALL commentating upon Shakspeare, there has been a radical error, never yet mentioned. It is the error of attempting to expound his characters—to account for their actions—to reconcile his inconsistencies—not as if they were the coinage of a human brain, but as if they had been actual existences upon earth. We talk of Hamlet the man, instead of Hamlet the *dramatis persona* —of Hamlet that God, in place of Hamlet that Shakspeare created. If Hamlet had really lived, and if the tragedy were an accurate record of his deeds, from this record (with some trouble) we might, it is true, reconcile his inconsistencies and settle to our satisfaction his true character. But the task becomes the purest absurdity when we deal only with a phantom. It is not (then) the inconsistencies of the acting man which we have as a subject of discussion—(although we proceed as if it were, and thus *inevitably* err,) but the whims and vacillations—the conflicting energies and indolences of the poet. It seems to us little less than a miracle, that this obvious point should have been overlooked.

While on this topic we may as well offer an ill-considered opinion of our own as to the *intention of the poet* in the delineation of the Dane. It must have been well known to Shakspeare, that a leading feature in certain more intense classes of intoxication, (from whatever cause,) is an almost irresistible impulse to counterfeit a farther degree of excitement than actually exists. Analogy would lead any thoughtful person to suspect the same impulse in madness—where beyond doubt it is manifest. This, Shakspeare *felt*—not thought. He felt it through his marvellous power of *identification* with humanity at large— the ultimate source of his magical influence upon mankind. He wrote of Hamlet as if Hamlet he were; and having, in the first instance, imagined his hero excited to partial insanity by the disclosures of the ghost—he (the poet) *felt* that it was natural he should be impelled to exaggerate the insanity.

I HAVE seen many computations respecting the greatest amount of erudition attainable by an individual in his lifetime; but these computations are falsely based, and fall infinitely beneath the truth. It is true that, *in general,* we retain, we remember to available purpose, scarcely one-hundredth part of what we read; yet there *are* minds which not only retain *all* receipts, but keep them at compound interest forever. Again:—were every man supposed to read *out,* he could read, of course, very little, even in half a century; for, in such case, each individual word must be dwelt upon in some degree. But, in reading to ourselves, at the ordinary rate of what is called "light reading," we scarcely *touch* one word in ten. And, even physically considered, knowledge breeds knowledge, as gold gold; for he who reads really much, finds his capacity to read increase in geometrical ratio. The *helluo librorum* will but glance at the page which detains the ordinary reader some minutes; and the difference in the absolute *reading* (its uses considered), will be in favor of the *helluo,* who will have winnowed the matter of which the *tyro* mumbled both the seeds and the chaff. A deep-rooted and strictly continuous habit of reading will, with certain classes of intellect, result in an instinctive and seemingly magnetic appreciation of a thing written; and now the student reads by pages just as other men by words. Long years to come, with a careful analysis of the mental process, may even render this species of appreciation a common thing. It may be taught in the schools of our descendants of the tenth or twentieth generation. It may become the method of the mob of the eleventh or twenty-first. And should these matters come to pass—as they will—there will be in them no more legitimate cause for wonder than there is, today, in the marvel that, syllable by syllable, men comprehend what, letter by letter, I now trace upon this page.

Is it not a law that need has a tendency to engender the thing needed?

LET A MAN succeed ever so evidently—ever so demonstrably—in many different displays of *genius*, the envy of criticism will agree with the popular voice in denying him more than *talent* in any. Thus a poet who has achieved a great (by which I mean an effective) poem, should be cautious not to distinguish himself in any other walk of Letters. In especial—let him make no effort in Science—unless anonymously, or with the view of waiting patiently the judgment of posterity. Because universal or even versatile geniuses have rarely or never been known, *therefore*, thinks the world, none such can ever be. A "therefore" of this kind is, with the world, conclusive. But what is the *fact*, as taught us by analysis of mental power? Simply, that *highest* genius—that the genius which all men instantaneously acknowledge as such—which acts upon individuals, as well as upon the mass, by a species of magnetism incomprehensible but irresistible and *never resisted*—that this genius which demonstrates itself in the simplest gesture—or even by the absence of all—this genius which speaks without a voice and flashes from the unopened eye—is but the result of generally large mental power existing in a state of *absolute proportion*—so that no one faculty has undue predominance. *That* factitious "genius"—that "genius" in the popular sense—which is but the manifestation of the abnormal predominance of some one faculty over all the others—and, of course, at the expense and to the detriment, of all the others—is a result of mental disease or rather, of organic malformation of mind:—it is this and nothing more. Not only will such "genius" fail, if turned aside from the path indicated by its predominant faculty; but, even when pursuing this path —when producing those works in which, certainly, it is *best* calculated to succeed—will give unmistakable indications of *unsoundness*, in respect to general intellect. Hence, indeed, arises the just idea that

Great wit to madness nearly is allied.

I say "*just* idea;" for by "great wit," in this case, the poet intends precisely the pseudo-genius to which I refer. The true

161

genius, on the other hand, is necessarily, if not universal in its manifestations, at least capable of universality; and if, attempting all things, it succeeds in one rather better than in another, this is merely an account of a certain bias by which *Taste* leads it with more earnestness in the one direction than in the other. With equal zeal, it would succeed equally in all.

To sum up our results in respect to this very simple, but much *vexata quaestio:*—

What the world calls "genius" is the state of mental disease arising from the undue predominance of some one of the faculties. The works of such genius are never sound in themselves and, in especial, always betray the general mental insanity.

The *proportion* of the mental faculties, in a case where the general mental power is *not* inordinate, gives that result which we distinguish as *talent:*—and the talent is greater or less, first, as the general mental power is greater or less; and, secondly, as the proportion of the faculties is more or less absolute.

The proportion of the faculties, in a case where the mental power is inordinately great, gives that result which *is* the true *genius* (but which, on account of the proportion and seeming simplicity of its works, is seldom acknowledged to *be* so;) and the genius is greater or less, first, as the general mental power is more or less inordinately great; and, secondly, as the proportion of the faculties is more or less absolute.

An objection will be made:—that the greatest excess of mental power, however proportionate, does not seem to satisfy our idea of genius, unless we have, in addition, sensibility, passion, energy. The reply is, that the "absolute proportion" spoken of, when applied to inordinate mental power, gives, as a result, the appreciation of Beauty and a horror of Deformity which we call sensibility, together with that intense vitality, which is implied when we speak of "Energy" or "Passion."

A NEW poem from Moore calls to mind that critical opinion respecting him which had its origin, we believe, in the dogmatism of Coleridge—we mean the opinion that he is essentially the poet of *fancy*—the term being employed in contradistinction to *imagination*. "The fancy," says the author of the "Ancient Mariner," in his *Biographia Literaria*, "the fancy combines, the imagination creates." And this was intended, and has been received, as a distinction. If so at all, it is one without a difference; without even a difference of *degree*. The fancy as nearly creates as the imagination; and neither creates in any respect. All novel conceptions are merely unusual combinations. The mind of man can *imagine* nothing which has not really existed; and this point is susceptible of the most positive demonstration —see the Baron de Bielfeld, in his *"Premiers Traits de L'Erudition Universelle,"* 1767. It will be said, perhaps, that we can imagine a *griffin*, and that a griffin does not exist. Not the griffin certainly, but its component parts. It is a mere compendium of known limbs and features—of known qualities. Thus with all which seems to be *new*—which appears to be a *creation* of intellect. It is resoluble into the old. The wildest and most vigorous effort of mind cannot stand the test of this analysis.

*　*　*

Many a schoolboy . . . is finally rejoiced at discovering his own imagination to surpass that of the author, since the monsters destroyed by Jack are only about forty feet in height, and he himself has no trouble in imagining some of one hundred and forty. The fairy of Shelley is not a mere compound of incongruous natural objects, inartificially put together, and unaccompanied by any *moral* sentiment; but a being, in the illustration of whose nature some physical elements are used collaterally as adjuncts, while the main concept springs immediately, *or thus apparently springs*, from the brain of the poet, enveloped in the moral sentiments of grace, of colour, of motion—of the beautiful, of the *mystical*, of the august—in short, of the ideal.

The truth is that the just disinction between the fancy and the imagination (and which is still but a distinction *of degree*) is involved in the consideration of the *mystic*. We give this as an idea of our own, altogether. We have no authority for our opinion—but do not the less firmly hold it. The term *mystic* is here employed in the sense of Augustus William Schlegel, and of most other German critics. It is applied by them to that class of composition in which there lies beneath the transparent upper current of meaning an under or *suggestive* one. What we vaguely term the *moral* of any sentiment is its mystic or secondary expression. It has the vast force of an accompaniment in music. This vivifies the air; that spiritualizes the *fanciful* conception, and lifts it into the *ideal*.

This theory will bear, we think, the most rigorous tests which can be made applicable to it, and will be acknowledged as tenable by all who are themselves imaginative. If we carefully examine those poems, or portions of poems, or those prose romances, which mankind have been accustomed to designate as *imaginative* (for an instinctive feeling leads us to employ properly the term whose full import we have still never been able to define), it will be seen that all so designated are remarkable for the *suggestive* character which we have discussed. They are strongly *mystic*, in the proper sense of the word. We will here only call to the reader's mind, the "Prometheus Vinctus" of AEschylus; the *Inferno* of Dante; the "Destruction of Numantia" by Cervantes; the "Comus" of Milton; the "Ancient Mariner," the "Christabel," and the "Kubla Khan" of Coleridge; the "Nightingale" of Keats; and, most especially, the "Sensitive Plant" of Shelley, and the *Undine* of De La Motte Fouqué. These two latter poems (for we call them both such) are the finest possible examples of the purely *ideal*. There is little of fancy here, and everything of imagination. With each note of the lyre is heard a ghostly, and not always a distinct, but an august and soul-exalting echo. In every glimpse of beauty presented, we catch, through long and wild vistas, dim bewildering visions of a far more ethereal beauty *beyond*. But not so in poems which the world has always persisted in terming *fanciful*. Here the upper current is often exceedingly brilliant and beautiful; but then men *feel* that this upper current *is all*. No Naiad voice addresses them *from below*. The notes of the air of the song do not tremble with the according tones of the accompaniment.

INDEX OF TITLES

INDEX OF FIRST LINES